CHOOSING THE
RIGHT PRACTICE LOCATION

"This is a book I wish I had my hands on before I started my practice seven years ago. Most dentists have the aspiration of going solo from their dental school days; however, on reading this book, dentists would enter the business world with their eyes open. Topics such as PPOs, practice locations, and taxes are far from a dental student's mind, let alone retirement. There were many excerpts in this book that I learnt through trial and error—some for which I paid dearly.

"Jayme Amos has written this book in a concise and easy-to-read fashion that helps clarify dental business situations for both the novice and the experienced. There are several important tools that I missed in my practice that I plan on incorporating since reading the book. This is a MUST-READ!"

—Unni Menon, DDS
Successfully purchased, built and sold a practice before the age of 30

"*Choosing the Right Practice Location* is a smart investment for the seasoned dentist looking for a new office location, a dental student contemplating future options, a young dentist ready to open their first practice, and everyone else who is involved in the quickly evolving profession of dentistry. Not investing in this book could cost you tens of thousands of dollars. It's an easy read with every step and consideration broken out point by point with real life examples. Take a couple hours to read this book and save yourself a lot of aggravation and money."

—Bill Neumann
Publisher, Efficiency In Group Practice / Founder, Dental Sales Pro

"Jayme's book, *Dentistry's Guide: Choosing the Right Practice Location*, is flat-out a must-read for every dentist who might ever consider moving to a new location or opening a new practice. I wish I had it to help me choose my dental office location 10 years ago when I opened my first office. The best news is: I've got it NOW for my next location!

"As soon as I finished Jayme's book, I sent a note to every single one of my ClearPath Society® Members with a simple directive: GET IT NOW and read it. Jayme provides a clear, easy-to-follow blueprint with examples on how to choose the right location for your next office—and why. His 12-point checklist will make your life easier and make your next location choice a far more profitable one. Ignore his book at your own, very costly peril. It should be in the hands of every dentist—no, make that every practice-based professional in America—immediately."

—*Jerry A. Jones*
CEO SofTouch Dental, Salem, Oregon
www.JerryJonesDirect.com / www.ClearPathSociety.com

"Starting, moving, or buying a practice can be a very stressful and exciting time at any stage in one's career. With all the complex moving parts involved in the process, it can be very easy to mishandle or overlook certain aspects that could potentially cost you your practice. Jayme has done a great service to the industry by lending his unique perspective and expertise on the subject, giving dentists very useful tools to help them avoid common blunders. This book is a great place to start for those of you beginning your journey toward practice ownership, especially because the author is able to make a complex subject seem so simple."

—*Steven Casella, DMD*
Owner, Casella Dental, West Chester, Pennsylvania

CHOOSING THE RIGHT PRACTICE LOCATION

ISBN: 978-0-9897803-0-8

Published by:
IP Publishing

Editing, cover, and book design by Stacey Aaronson

Printed in the USA

DENTISTRY'S GUIDE

CHOOSING THE
RIGHT
PRACTICE LOCATION:

THE OVERLOOKED WAYS
DEMOGRAPHICS, PPOs,
TAXES & RETIREMENT
ARE LINKED TO
THIS CRITICAL DECISION

JAYME AMOS

IP PUBLISHING

We shape our buildings and thereafter, they shape us.

—Winston Churchill

CONTENTS

THE 9 TOOLS

AUTHOR'S NOTE

What a journey.

When our team first published this book in 2013, we had no idea the impact on the industry would so positively affect as many dentists as it did.

Now, this powerful and practical book has become a bestseller, lead to discussions with the ADA, become a series of posts on Dental Town, been resourced by major industry leaders (like Academy of Dental CPAs, IgniteDDS, Dental Entrepreneur, Wellness Springs Dental, and ClearPath Society), created thousands of visitors per month on our website, and reached readers worldwide.

After working with dentists for over a decade, I've seen the journey of practice ownership up close and personal. The results have been an inspiration to me.

It's been an incredible honor to walk alongside these doctors, finding the best ways to build and grow the practices they've dreamed of owning for years.

Now, in an attempt to say thank you to the industry that has so generously granted us trust, we're adding new resources in this edition of *Choosing the Right Practice Location.*

BONUS MATERIAL

If you're like a lot of our clients, you're looking for detailed training and guidance to follow a proven process. If that's you and you want to explore those options right now, flip to page 119 to find a list of resources you can access right away.

See the resources online at:

www.HowToOpenADentalOffice.com/resources

Enjoy the information we've prepared for you and experience the fullness of the journey through practice ownership!

Best,

Jayme

PS: Want to hear a personal message from me?
Go here to get access to a message available only to people who own a copy this book:

www.HowToOpenADentalOffice.com/message

Training in Your Car

Now you can access our most relevant tools on your commute!

Learn the latest techniques for skills, new patients, profitability, and practice growth.

Subscribe now to the Ideal Practices podcast and get our most current thoughts for free.

Ideal Practices: The Dental Podcast for Practice Ownership

www.HowToOpenADentalOffice.com/podcast

What You'll Learn in This Book

❖ Where one small difference between two local communities will cost you $50,000 in the first year of your new practice

❖ How participating with insurance companies can be ugly ... but *partnering* with them could also be the one factor yielding you the most profitability

❖ How you can analyze thousands of demographic data points for your new location search in any region with a simple 12-point checklist in less than five minutes

❖ A true story of local politics and a sewer-line battle with the EPA that almost cost one doctor hundreds of thousands of dollars

❖ How to choose a location that will strategically give you large "pops" of new patient growth over the years

❖ How choosing a location five miles further away could change your retirement net worth by at least $1,000,000

❖ Why your sign shouldn't be anything more than boring

❖ Why landlords secretly want you to negotiate price—and why you need to be very careful in that negotiation

❖ Which 12 demographics criteria matter to new dental practices ... and which two could determine the fate of your long-term profitability

❖ And much more!

INTRODUCTION

E very dentist who plans to create a new office must face a very serious, one-word question:

Where?

The decision will affect the rest of your career as it becomes the trajectory for success from opening day forward. *Choosing the Right Practice Location* will give you clarity in the decision-making process, confidence in your final choice, and all the tools you'll need to evaluate your options.

What you won't find in this book is the "how" of opening a dental office. Knowledge regarding *how* will be necessary in the months following your Location Decision, but first you need to determine *where*. When the time comes, you can access an extensive library of learning all about the *how* on:

www.HowToOpenADentalOffice.com

You can also access our acclaimed blog here, which has some of the most candid and revealing information about the topic. But prior to implementing the knowledge of *how*, it's crucial you have the right *where*. Without the right *where*, as the saying goes, you go *nowhere*.

The nine tools in this book will create a clear path for you to find the right location the first time. You need to choose your location wisely because there's so much on the line.

But before we dig into the material at hand, you probably want to know a little bit about where the knowledge and experience comes from in this discussion.

· · ·

I've been working with dentists for nearly a decade. What I have to share with you are proven concepts that have helped the wonderful people I've grown to know and respect deeply in the dental community. My hope is that the tools you'll find here will embolden you with energy and passion for what will likely be the biggest investment of your life.

We are in what the business world has spent decades calling a "Cottage Industry," which could be described as wall-street-speak for "not a big enough industry to put large amounts of resources into." I feel quite the opposite, and it seems we as a dental community have attracted growing attention from some large banks and venture capital groups. The attention received by the dental community reminds me that dentistry matters in many ways— namely, that when caring dentists provide excellent clinical care, strong profits can be the result. And there are some compelling reasons why profits *should* be the result.

Try to calculate all the investment, energy and risk associated with being a dentist:

- ❖ The average dental education is clocking in near $200,000–$400,000 (excluding undergraduate requirements).

- ❖ Continuing education is a pursuit for your entire career.

- ❖ Legal liability is devastating and a few vultures exploit it.

- ❖ HIPAA and OSHA are required.

- ❖ Staff needs are significant.

- ❖ Dentists work for 7–11 months before they start to make a profit for themselves and their families.

- ❖ Emergencies are real and they do disrupt meaningful personal time with your family.

- ❖ And worst of all, dentists have the highest cost of building a new office per square foot of any industry.

Yes, you read that correctly. It's been said that out of *all* industries, the small business with the highest set-up cost per square foot is dentistry.

The opportunity for profit and satisfaction is high, but it can cost $500,000 to get everything set up in your new location. It's for all these reasons that it's imperative you design, build, and find the right location the first time. You don't want to do this again if you don't need to—and if you do it right, you won't have to.

Your opportunity to enjoy a fulfilling career is wonderful, your ability to care for patients is unlike any other field, and your potential to provide well for yourself and your family is excellent. But the truth is your financial risks are quite high. It's important we get your Location Decision right so you can have the highest chance of success.

For the record, I'm not a dentist.

On the topic of location selection, that's good news for you. Those who spend their career chair-side strive to become excellent in that clinical role, and our society is very fortunate to have the doctors who dedicate themselves to improving their skills. But to develop a keen understanding of all the elements that comprise a well-crafted dental office Location Decision, it's crucial that you find someone who has a long, successful, dental-specific track record in the *where* of your office. Your future success depends on it.

I've spent nearly a decade investing in my education in the start-up and development of successful dental practices, and the results have been wonderful for my clients.

What I've found is that your future practice success involves much more than the clinical skills you work so hard to develop. In today's competitive, high-stakes dental economy, it's critical that the people on your team have deep expertise in three areas:

1. Launching new dental practices
2. Real estate buying and leasing
3. Small business growth

By including people on your team with a unique blend of knowledge on these three topics, your chances of success improve dramatically.

As I've invested the last 15 years in developing and improving those skills, I've witnessed tangible positive effects on our industry.

When I was 21 years old, fresh out of school with a degree in International Business, I signed my first business lease for a start-up I co-founded and grew to a million dollars of revenue in its first year of operation. Shortly after that, I bought my first rental property, a duplex, and went on through the years to own dozens of residential properties on the east coast.

As a managing partner and investor in a nationwide franchised financial firm, I was asked to participate in multiple millions of dollars of leasing commitments from the Midwest to the East Coast, all of which involved site selection, construction, and opening day. And now, I've worked side by side for nearly a decade with my dentist-clients, coordinating growth on their behalf and acting as their business wingman with excellent results.

I tell you all this only to say I've seen and negotiated quite a few site locations, witnessed a couple of botched projects, created profitable dental practice growth strategies, and been tasked to find perfect locations in cities I've never visited before—and all of these pieces of my history blend into a dentist's ideal Location Decision.

Now I work closely with hundreds of dentists, many of whom have become dear friends to me. With practice owners choosing to work with my team to design, build, equip, and open their dream office, I've helped look at hundreds of dental locations and participated in finding the best possible sites. We visit locations, coordinate office lease reviews, create clear goals and plans for construction, help find the best lenders, assist in matchmaking with motivated insurance companies, and much more. It's a process that's exciting to a guy like me who likes numbers, negotiating, legalese, and tight timelines.

My team becomes a quasi-quarterback in the all-consuming and oftentimes overwhelming experience of a new practice project, being as involved in the process as the dentist desires. It's a role we take more seriously than most expect, and it's one in which we take tremendous pride.

On the specific topic of the Location Decision, there is so much at stake for my dental client, and because of that I put a mountain of energy and emotion into successful selection and negotiation of their space. The result? It works. My clients have inspiring success stories, pride in their locations, and confidence that the home of their practice was the right choice.

You can do this too!

Many ask me what the entire process looks like. While the full explanation is the topic of a much longer conversation, I would summarize it by saying this:

The process is a transformation—of a building *and* a doctor.

The transformative process starts with you, moves into building a facility, and ends with a new you. When you respond to a deeply-rooted desire to work in a practice space that reflects your clinical skills, your pride in your profession, and your commitment to excellent clinical care, your life begins to change. It might sound like a high calling and a glorified experience, but every piece of it is rich and full and it becomes a life moment you'll never forget.

Those who have crafted their own dental practices are in an exclusive membership of doctors who spend many hours of their life experiencing a new level of fulfillment and accomplishment that many say is indescribable. For some, the transformative process starts when they're as young as children; for others the desire materializes when they feel they've plateaued in their experience as an associate. Regardless of your starting point, your situation will lead you to a new level of professional and life fulfillment through this project, and your efforts to pursue this fully will be rewarded well.

This book discusses the Location Decision, which is usually the step immediately following financing and loan discussions. After the Location Decision, we begin an extensive customized design process where our design team incorporates a 40-point checklist and multiple face-to-face discussions to craft the perfect floor plan for your new office, culminating in a 3D virtual walkthrough of the space in its digital glory.

We then work with you to coordinate with contractors and guide you to the best possible construction choices available for the unique needs of your specific dental practice. The process moves forward to architectural and engineering planning and then moves through the meat grinder of local politics—some are enjoyable to work with, others make me feel like I'm as smart as a caveman with all their inventive ways of delaying projects.

The process includes an inordinate number of moving parts along the way, from plumbing to timed dispensing of funds, from integration of technologies to carving paths for those of the future. Topics as diverse as signage, marketing, storage space for supplies, cubic feet per user, and properly sized air lines are a few of the innumerable reasons why this process can have so many twists and turns.

But in the end, the final product—the final home—is yours. It's your mark on your community and your *pièce de résistance*. This will be a place that's a physical representation of all your years of education and preparation and will enable you to provide care for friends and family for years. With the tools in this book, I hope to inspire, educate, and motivate you toward success.

And it all starts with *where*.

I'm not holding anything back. While many like to cling tightly to their knowledge, I believe that by sharing it freely, everyone in our "cottage industry" wins. And that's good for all of us.

Get ready—your new practice is probably closer than you think.

Here's to you and your success!

DENTISTRY'S LOCATION
DECISION OVERVIEW

For existing practices considering building a new office, the Location Decision will be an encouraging exploration of the structurally supporting factors *outside* of your current practice walls that have lead to your success to this point. This will uncover all of the components external to your practice that we can replicate and improve on in your next location. It will also be an opportunity to help you choose a new location that is *at least* as good as your existing location, whether or not you stay in the same zip code of your current practice.

For doctors who are building their first practice, these nine tools will help you stay focused on the crucial Location Decision factors to give you the greatest chance at getting the facility of your dreams—and the one that has the potential to grow profitably for you in the most predictable way. After we find you the best place on the map, you can then explore the exciting process of creating your physical space.

It's been said that building a beautiful new office is the easy part. Building it in a *location* that will earn you a comfortable living is something totally different. From this point forward, this discussion will focus on giving you the maximum amount of understanding on the topic of choosing the right location for your future practice.

Probably 99% of dentists who think about creating a new office have fewer than three experiences choosing locations for any long-term real estate transaction. That's certainly not an inherent problem in most areas of your life, but for this stage of your new practice, experience with that narrow of a range could limit your potential, and you have too much on the line to risk it.

Your Location Decision is likely the one with more impact on your future success than any other in the new practice process. This puts dentists in a vulnerable and financially risky position, and unfortunately, this process is often one lead by a single financially motivated person—the realtor. We'll discuss some strategies to work with realtors in a later chapter, but for now I'll say that I admire many of my realtor friends; the problem is I have yet to find more than a handful with any true dental-relevant experience.

The limitations of experience by a key person like a realtor who doesn't have dental-specific experience can result in decades of unreached potential in your practice. Regardless of the professional, don't let any person tell you they have an understanding of the needs of a dental practice unless they've gone through the entire process at least a dozen times. Anything less could leave you open to some very expensive learning experiences.

You may be thinking:

> *What about the "perfect building" I've driven past so many times?*

> *Are all these location planning tools really necessary if I already have my eyes on that building?*

I've heard "That would make a great dental practice" about many attractive locations. But before you choose the right *building*, we must first focus on the right *location*. Prior to going through the examination of the following nine tools, the emotional feelings about a structure are our only guiding principle—and feelings unfortunately don't ensure success for a dental practice.

Feelings and emotions are what make us human and for that, I cherish and embrace them—the joy and disappointments of living would be all but worthless without the gift we can enjoy in emotions. But in the very high-stakes Location Decision process, we need to limit our emotional drivers and instead focus on subjective criteria first. You'll have moments of enormous levels of pride, excitement, passion, and energy about your new building, but those should come *after* we have put the Location Decision tools to work for us.

Let's look at an example:

> We were working with a pediatric dentist who was upgrading his practice by moving to a better facility and nicer area in town, and he had two very good options in our final decision process. Real estate was limited in that town, but both properties held nearly the same attributes:
>
> | | |
> |---|---|
> | ❖ parking | ❖ size |
> | ❖ zip code | ❖ demographics |
> | ❖ signage | ❖ and more |
> | ❖ traffic | |
>
> The doctor wanted to own his next practice, and since both of these properties could be rented or purchased, we came to this conclusion: Each of the two buildings, based on our nine tools, was essentially the same, good choice. We brought the decision down to his

personal feelings on the properties, and in the end, it boiled down to his gut feeling because everything else was subjectively ideal for a new facility.

It's my hope that you'll find the tools here to be pragmatic and subjective, relying on the countless examples available to us.

Together, we'll uncover what will lead you to a rockstar-like successful practice.

Your process and experience in your Location Decision are about to be transformed with the capabilities in nine simple tools that will empower you to know exactly how to make your future practice most successful.

• • •

WHAT IS THE IDEAL OUTCOME IF YOU USE THESE NINE TOOLS?

You will be able to lead the process, not have the process and its members lead you.

Dentists are trained and excellent at providing oral healthcare, not necessarily choosing the best practice location. The success criteria for a dental practice's location are vastly different from the requirements of any other business or industry, and we can't let any professionals tell us otherwise. By using these nine simple tools, you'll be far ahead of anyone on your Practice Project Team, and you'll have the necessary direction and information to know the criteria your new practice needs. You'll also save time by eliminating poor location options from your search at the very beginning of your process, and you'll save large sums of money by avoiding the expenses of locations that should never be used for dental practices in the first place.

WHAT IS THE BEST THING THAT CAN HAPPEN AS A RESULT OF USING THESE TOOLS?

Within 60 minutes of reading this book, you'll have an outline of the nine most important aspects to analyze your Location Decision, which will give you 90% of all the data you'll need before making the final decision. The remaining pieces of information you'll need are related to project-specific issues that should be discussed on a project-by-project basis. My team would be honored to have those discussions with you when that time comes.

As soon as you work through the nine tools, you'll have all you need to start the process and begin to lead your Practice Project Team, getting them focused on the search for the ideal location based on your predetermined, accurate search criteria. You'll be able to lead the team clearly and effectively with total confidence toward the right town, area, street, and even intersection that's best for your new practice. These nine tools are prepared in a way that can assist in successfully planning the search for nearly any new practice location in the country.

WHAT IS THE WORST THING THAT CAN HAPPEN IF YOU DON'T IMPLEMENT THE NINE LOCATION DECISION TOOLS?

Those who choose not to use these nine tools will find themselves frustrated, wasting money, spending weeks and months of unnecessary searching, and vulnerable to choosing a location that will set them back decades from their financial and professional goals. A poor Location Decision can cost hundreds of thousands of dollars and unrecoverable professional capabilities. Don't let this happen to you—invest the time now to reap rewards for decades to come.

Now, prepare for the rest of your career to begin.

LOCATION DECISION TOOL #1:

DEMOGRAPHICS WILL
CHANGE YOUR WORLD:

THE ESSENTIAL 12-POINT CHECKLIST

If there were one tool of the nine that I would say has the most powerful impact on your financial success, it would be the proper analysis of demographics. For that reason, we'll spend a large portion of the discussion on this topic.

According to Wikipedia, demographics are the quantifiable statistics of a given population. That's a long way of saying "people, broken down into categories and numbers." For existing practices, this will be an interesting analysis of the factors that have lead to your current success, and it will help you determine if those factors are serving you well in your current locale.

HOW MIGHT DEMOGRAPHICS BE HELPFUL TO A NEW DENTAL PRACTICE?

There's a popular town in southeastern Pennsylvania that I'll leave nameless. It's quaint, has beautiful architecture, deep historical charm, and clearly has a higher-than-average income level as evidenced by the looks of the homes and cars around town. You may have an area like this on your list of ideal practice locations.

What could be better than living in that home just off Main Street where you could walk to the local coffee shop on your stroll to the office each morning? But here's the problem in this particular town: twenty-four other dentists are already taking that same morning stroll. The town is saturated. When a sponge is full and overflowing with water, it's called supersaturated. If you open a dental practice in that quaint town, super-saturation will arrive. You will forever stroll to an office that seems like it has no patients. That's not a good thing if you have loan payments, a mortgage, or a grocery bill. Our antidote will be demographics as they will be our guiding light to avoid a disaster scenario like this one.

The use of demographics during your searching process, with a keen eye for dental-specific data, will hold the key to understanding this and countless other potential problems before we even get our hopes up for a quaint town like the one we discussed. Demographics are crucial to the success of your new practice, but the numbers are endless, creating glazed-over eyes and a high possibility of analysis paralysis. Few know exactly which metrics matter most to a dentist's success.

But as long as you have a strong understanding of the right demographics information, you will have confidence in your choice and a dramatically higher potential for good new patient flow, greater financial success, lower stress levels, and long-term satisfaction with your ability to care for patients in the way you desire.

My team and I like to use a 12-point checklist for demographics reports, but the most potent metric won't be found in any census data: it's the Population-to-Doctor ratio (PDR). I've been shocked to find that our dental community doesn't make a bigger deal about the Population-to-Doctor ratio when doctors plan their new location. For general dentists, if you determine that a defined area has a bare minimum ratio of least a 2000:1, you'll avoid being poorly positioned.

Why is that?

All practices (even part-time ones) need at least 1000 patients to stay busy. So if you have fewer than 2000 patients residing in the town for every dentist in that same town, you'll have a high probability of growth problems in the future. We all know that not all patients in a town will go to the dentist, and as a matter of fact, I've seen it estimated by reputable dental organizations that only 50% of the population regularly sees a dentist.

**As a general principle, you want the
Population-to-Doctor ratio to be as large as possible.
The bigger, the better.**

But there is much more to consider beyond that key ratio. What follows is our 12-Point Demographics Checklist—any of which could make or break your decision to choose a location—that I review with clients. We'll use a real-life example so that we can apply reality to the checklist, and we'll use a town I love to visit named Phoenixville, PA, the home of the movie *The Blob* (the 1950s hit about a big black blob that consumes everything in its way. It ends with a climactic scene in which people run out of the movie theater. That scene was filmed in the local downtown theater, still in existence today). The data I use is accurate and gathered from various sources I use for clients.

In this examination of the 12-point checklist, we'll see how many items on the list we can "check off" to see if Phoenixville could qualify under these criteria.

1. POPULATION

The number of people who reside in that specific area.

- ❖ This number should be a minimum of 2,000 people as you will be attempting to attract people within the searched area.

- ❖ A number lower than 2,000 could mean you're too far from other complementary industries, homes, employers, and general traffic that will benefit your practice.

There is no negative effect on your practice success with high population numbers. The exception to the minimum of 2,000 people is if your desired town is adjacent to another community that would help exceed the minimum.

For instance, if you have a small town of 500, just three miles from a town of 6000 people, it's perfectly acceptable to count those people in your population. The rule of thumb in this exception is the three-mile radius.

Now, in our example case of Phoenixville, PA, we have approximately 16,000 residents, which means "Population" passes the test.

☑ On our checklist, Phoenixville receives 1 checkmark to make it 1 for 1!

2. POPULATION CHANGE – 1 YEAR

This is the anticipated change in population growth for the year following the date you gather the demographics data.

This predictive number is a wonderful tool that shouldn't be overlooked, and in it resides a massive amount of power that can work *for* you or *against* you. Just imagine if you have hundreds of new people moving into your town every year, you would have a wonderful opportunity for easier new patient flow with proper marketing.

While not all towns or dentists are that fortunate, a nominal level of population growth shouldn't dissuade you from considering a location. What should dissuade you is a quickly shrinking population. My suggestion is to cautiously avoid towns with negative population growth, but only eliminate those locations from your search if the population growth is worse than –1% per year.

> Let's consider our Phoenixville example. Population Growth there is anticipated to grow approximately 1% per year, better than the state's average.
>
>  On our checklist, Phoenixville now has 2 out of 2 checks!

3. POPULATION CHANGE – 5 YEAR

The five-year growth rate is also important, especially for those dentists who plan on leasing their office space, since the majority of leases run for a minimum of five years.

Phoenixville qualifies again. Check 3 out of 3!

4. POPULATION CHANGE – 10 YEAR

The rationale for analyzing the ten-year population change is very similar to the previous population growth categories, but this category has the power to help carry your practice well beyond the first extension on your lease. This also bodes well for those who opt to own their real estate.

> Phoenixville, with approximately 1% anticipated growth per year over the next 10 years is a good, steady pattern and qualifies again.

 Check 4!

5. INCOME – PER CAPITA

Per capita income is a measurement that calculates the total amount of income throughout the town, divided by the total number of people who live in that town.

More income is generally better for a standard start-up general practice, but more importantly, it's wise to compare the per capita income to the state and national averages. The most common start-up practices don't intend to have their primary delivery of care offered to the lowest of income levels, but this is a decision for each individual doctor, and that data will be found in the Per Capita statistic.

> For Phoenixville, we'll assume we're looking for a practice not primarily focused on the lower income level population. Phoenixville's higher-than-average income levels relative to state and national averages fit the model. The national and

state averages are approximately $27,000, and this town has approximately $33,000 per capita income.

 Check 5!

6. INCOME – HOUSEHOLD

Household income is exactly what it sounds like. It adds all the income available, on average, for each residential address in the town. The process of analyzing this number is similar to per capita income (comparing to state and national averages), but it also gives you an accurate estimate of the number of people in a family.

By dividing the household income by the per-capita income, we'll find the average number of people per household. This is excellent information to hold, assuming you know the kind of dentistry you want to do. In the case of Phoenixville, the presence of families— and therefore a potential for long-term practice relationships with those families—is very good.

> In this town, household income is approximately $73,000. If we divide $73,000 by the per capita income of $33,000, we calculate 2.22 people per residential address. This shows a strong likelihood of healthy, growing families. Here again, Phoenixville qualifies with household income.
>
> Check 6 out of 6 total marks on our checklist of 12!

7. INCOME – DISPOSABLE

Disposable income is important to dentistry because of the shift in patient interests toward more cosmetic care, and the looming changes for employers' offering of dental insurance benefits for employees (I write and speak about this topic and its relevance for dentists often because the topic could change our dental community dramatically, even if the laws don't directly mention dentistry!).

For these reasons and many others obvious ones, disposable income is better if it's higher. The comprehension of this number is not complex, but recognition and awareness of the number is quite important. Lack of disposable income may imply a long-term strain on your new practice's ability to thrive.

Phoenixville has a relatively high level of disposable income at approximately $48,000.

 Check 7!

8.   MASS TRANSIT

The existence of mass transit, bus, and rail lines bodes well for most towns and cities. The residents in that town will have more access to jobs in larger metropolitan areas, and they'll simultaneously have a greater likelihood of not having to move if their job is terminated because of the public transportation available to them.

For the purposes of your research, the availability of public transportation can be loosely correlated with homeowner stability. While the Mass Transit criterion isn't of primary concern, it does add an extra benefit to a long list of other healthy criteria.

For Phoenixville, the mass transit options are mediocre, at best. Only medium-distance bus routes are available and there is no subway or other rail transportation available. In this criterion, Phoenixville does not get a check.

We're now at 7 out of 8 total in our count.

9. AVERAGE AGE IN LOCAL POPULATION

The average age and median age for any location is very important in your Location Decision. I would highly recommend finding a community with an average age between 35 and 50. Why? Those ages are most likely to be settled, anchored to the community, at a higher income level in their career, most likely to have children, and still offer a long-term patient relationship with your practice.

If you're looking at opening a start-up practice, I would highly recommend finding a community on the lower end of the 35-50 age spectrum. If you're moving your practice to a new location, I suggest aiming for the middle or higher ages in that range as it will offer plenty of early retirees and baby boomers with disposable income, while those patients still have decades of age to offer patient loyalty to your practice.

> Phoenixville is looking good as a potential location for start-up practices and an adequate option for existing practices with its average age of 39.

 8 out of 9 checks for Phoenixville

10. OWNER-OCCUPIED HOUSING

This is the number of or percentage of people in the community who own their own homes. The stability and life priorities that are typically associated with renters and home owners may not be politically correct, but in this case, the stereotypes are important to acknowledge as they are relevant and often accurate.

High renter populations will normally not have as much loyalty to a practice because they have a higher likelihood of moving than a homeowner. It's also more likely that a renter will be more emergency prone than their homeowner counterparts because of statistically lower personal wellness levels. Higher homeownership also implies long-term financial commitment to an area, thereby offering a more possible long-term length of patient loyalty.

For practice owners who are excellent at "converting" emergency patients into long-term or large-case success stories, a higher number of renters could be preferable, but I find the prevalence of those clinicians to be the exception. For the doctors who hope for more naturally likely long-term stability, higher homeownership levels are preferable.

> The preference of more homeowners over renters is a personal preference and could vary by doctor, but for the case of Phoenixville—with a ratio of 44% renters and 56% owners—I'll give them a vote of "toss up."
>
> Half a check is being awarded, making 8.5 out of 10 so far.

11. EMPLOYMENT RATE

The importance of this metric is rarely disputed unless your practice focuses on state-provided dental care, in which case it can be argued that higher unemployment may be a better fit for that practice's business model. For the purposes of this discussion, we'll assume higher employment is better, as the majority of practice owners target this population.

The current national average for unemployment is between 7% and 8% (at the time of publication of this book), which would lead me to suggest you aim for a community with an unemployment rate lower than that. You may be shocked to find that the unemployment rate can vary widely from town to town. For instance, Norristown—a town close to Phoenixville—is over 10%!

> Meanwhile, in Phoenixville, the unemployment rate is between 4% and 5%. Wow. Phoenixville, then, is in a better position than the country and some other locales.

 Check count: 9.5 out of 11

12. NUMBER OF DENTISTS

This may be the most important of all the criteria. Why? For starters, it's your profession, and it's good to know how many competitors you'll have to face when marketing for new patients. Some locations have the right mix of existing practices, others have surprisingly too many, and others have too few.

One might assume that fewer is better for a new practice's success, and typically that assumption is correct. But it's also important to note that a number dramatically too low could be a warning sign. Here's a true story to consider.

> A nearly unbelievable example is a client who found a seemingly wonderful opportunity to build a start-up practice in a town with plenty of population and only two other dentists. This doctor quickly signed the lease and got all the ducks in a row to get the practice launched as soon as possible. So what was the problem? Could there be a reason why there were so few dentists?

> The local government officials had been in a multi-year fight with the EPA for overages in their sewer system, a problem that would require this town to wrestle their water usage downward or face millions of dollars of federally required upgrades to their

sewer system. In other words, the town was trying to keep out high-water-use businesses to avoid upgrading their sewer system. The effect of this political drama left the doctor with a signed lease, no permission to begin construction, and months of pleading with local officials.

The powers of those local officials is on the level of deity in some towns, and in this situation, they held all the control over this doctor. After months of delays, proof pieces that showed minimal water usage, pre-purchasing of mechanical equipment, operatory equipment that used less water, and plenty of phone calls, the gracious elected officials granted the doctor a gift of benevolence: Yes. But only one operatory could be used! They would grant the doctor an annual review process where they would reconsider based on actual water use. Stunning but true.

The point I'm making here is that a number of dentists far *too low* may mean there is more to the story. But returning to a more likely reality and the more typical Location Decision discussion at hand, I can tell you that under normal circumstances, the metric of total number of dentists is nearly always better when it's lower. However, as a caveat, I suggest doing plenty of investigative work with other local businesses before signing the lease if the number looks too low.

According to the tools I use, there are 11 general dentists in Phoenixville. If you remember the first thought I shared with you at the beginning of our demographics conversation, the term "Population-to-Doctor Ratio" will come back to you.

Let's look at this for Phoenixville. Now, in a big city, 11 other dentists in the same town may not be a concern, but let's look at the Population-to-Doctor Ratio and see if "double digit" competition is problematic.

First, take the total population and divide by the number of dentists in the area:

$$16,000 / 11 = 1454$$

By my standards, this doesn't qualify as a healthy Patient-to-Doctor ratio and therefore is a fail for any dentist looking to open a new practice. For an existing practice looking to open a new location that already has a decade or more of patient loyalty, my conclusion would be different, though a poor ratio like that should cause some pause. The reality is that a Population-to-Doctor Ratio of 1454 is one that I would never advise a client who's building a new office to consider.

Our total number of checks is now 9.5 out of 12.

So how does this entire topic stack up as a case study? In the case of Phoenixville, I would say stay home and rent a copy of *The Blob* from Netflix. Even though the score of 9.5 out of 12 checks would sound appealing to the uninformed, I would advise you keep looking.

The primary reason is the all-too-important ratio. As you weigh your options, remember that no matter how attractive a town or a community seems to be, we must separate the emotions from the Location Decision for you to have the best chances of a practice success story. Phoenixville is a town I will continue to visit but not on Location Decision tours with clients anytime soon.

Crisis averted;
room for pursuit of the ideal practice still available.

The PDR Importance

The Population-to-Doctor-Ratio (PDR) is a powerful metric, indeed.

With a high PDR, you could generate a strong flow of new patients at a low cost; few practice owners would turn that offer down. But below, we'll discuss some cautionary examples of how the PDR, if used incorrectly, can create a terrible outcome for your future.

Simply stated, the PDR is just one of many factors to consider, even though it should take a position of high priority.

Surely, wherever you have lots of population and few dentists, there is a high likelihood that your practice will benefit from that disparity. In business school, this is called supply and demand. Lots of population supply and low provider demand in the region could make your practice the beneficiary to thousands of new patients.

If you desire new patients in your new office, it's imperative you find a region with a PDR in alignment with your vision. The cautionary note is that a higher PDR is only better if all the demographics and site selection efforts from that region are in alignment with your vision.

In other words, a higher PDR is better only when it includes the right kinds of patients for your vision *and* the right location selection for your vision.

For example, what good is a region with a high PDR if it only gets you a practice full of patients who have no teeth and no income?

Or, more seriously, what good is owning a new practice if the lease you just signed ruins your chances of building a future for your retirement (this happens, as discussed in chapter 6).

Or, what if your vision defines your Ideal Patient as a young family, but you accidentally open in a region with a high PDR flooded with a geriatric population?

Issues like these are avoidable, but doctors still deal with this all over the country.

A higher PDR isn't the solution.

An alignment of your specific vision *with* a high PDR is.

To create an understanding of this alignment, we take clients through a process called the Ideal Patient Multiplier. The results are outstanding when you're able to fully define, pursue, and attract the exact type of patient you enjoy helping.

Imagine your favorite patient. Now think of that specific person's name. What do you like about them? What treatment did they accept? Do you have an image of that patient? Now imagine a practice full of 2,000 of those patients. Would you enjoy working in that practice? Of course!

It's possible to choose a region that helps you attract the kinds of patients you desire, and the PDR plays an important role in that process. The Ideal Patient Multiplier helps our clients target their best patients so you have a practice you enjoy fully. All this information is used in our demographic analyses, our marketing efforts for practice owners, and even the design of the practice.

As part of your specific vision, the PDR is just one step in that process.

What happens when the PDR is ignored?

When the PDR is ignored, some doctors can unknowingly open their practice in a town with a low PDR. Some may be attracted to open a practice in a "pretty town"; unfortunately, many of those come with poor demographic criteria, and doctors unknowingly set themselves up for disappointment and financial hardship.

For them, the only path out is often a long and expensive route to growth; for others, the sole path is an indefinite part-time associateship just to pay the bills. With too few patients or too many dentists in the region, those doctors need an ambitious and well-funded marketing plan to offset the problem. Avoid becoming like some practice owners—who have to fight through years of expensive marketing plans by remembering the PDR—and using it as a piece of your total strategy.

**The PDR, while critical, must play only
a partial role in choosing the right location.**

For the purposes of this book and your future Practice Location, use a simple rule of thumb:

When the PDR is within 1,000 of the 2,000 PDR benchmark (for a total between 1,000 and 3,000), a comprehensive analysis must be performed—or you should look for another region altogether.

There are exceptions and misunderstandings to the rule of the PDR, three of which we'll discuss shortly. Some of the exceptions and additional considerations to include with the PDR are:

- ❖ A full competitive analysis of other practices
- ❖ 50 Point Demographics Comprehensive Analysis
- ❖ The Donut Hole Theory

- ❖ The potential of Insurance Partnering (discussed in chapter 7)
- ❖ An alignment of your clinical, financial, and personal vision
- ❖ The influential difference between the PDR and the I-PDR
- ❖ Commuter towns, bedroom communities, and transient towns
- ❖ Safe offsets to future population growth

Here, we'll address three misunderstood aspects of this metric.

PDR MISUNDERSTANDING #1

"The PDR doesn't apply to practice relocations."

First, if you have an existing patient base, the PDR will, in fact, have *less* impact on your Location Decision.

However, don't be fooled.

The PDR will still have a dramatic impact on your future growth.

For example, if you already have a practice with 3,000 patients and you plan on moving to another location, your practice is probably stable. If this is your situation, you may not be in need of 50–100 new patients per month, as we pursue for our start-up clients (for them, we combine the power of demographics *and* marketing, like in the 100 New Patients on Opening Day tools). For practice relocations, it is still wise to consider the PDR insomuch as you desire *future* new patient growth.

In our Phoenixville example, with a PDR of 1,454, your relocation practice in that town may be able to survive and maintain profitability based on your existing patients. Future growth potential, however, will be weakened as a result of the lower PDR. For some doctors in a relocation project, future growth isn't a high priority.

For the practice owners who want a relocation that maintains the maximum level of patients and simultaneously continues to grow their new-patient levels, we suggest a few specific strategies.

To have the best of both worlds, a practice looking to relocate might hire our firm for guidance to find excellent demographics *while* combining an effective strategy to maintain the majority of existing patients.

Recently, we worked with a client in Arizona who asked us to help him relocate. To do this, we analyzed multiple regions, uncovering a few with demographics that were good, but none in his region far exceeded the 2,000 PDR benchmark.

To counteract the lower PDR in those areas, we considered PPO Partnering (discussed in Chapter 7), structured a winning lease, used our 15 points of contractor negotiation to keep costs low, and combined all those strategies with a powerful marketing campaign.

The marketing campaign was elegant and continued to offset the low PDR level with new patients, even after the grand opening event.

By encouraging strong patient referrals with creative incentives specifically tied to the relocation project, we simultaneously increased new patients *and* deepened patient loyalty. Remember, this was all done during a practice relocation, which is frequently a concern for patient *loss*.

In this process, we used relationship-deepening marketing, basing it on patients co-creating the new office *with us*. These co-creating techniques work with relocation projects and start-ups.

To our surprise over the years, the co-creating marketing tools have a near magical effectiveness on deepening patient loyalty and new patient flow.

In these situations, we help clients take advantage of a fascinating truism:

Humans are more committed to the things they help create.

What are these "co-creating marketing tools"?

At the risk of diverting this chapter from a Practice Location discussion into a marketing one, let's look at an example you can use in your new office.

With this Arizona doctor's practice, we prepared a multi-part internal marketing strategy to involve and engage the patients in the process of opening the new office. Immediately after signing the lease on the new space, we selected three color schemes for the office, each appealing to the doctor, the staff, and his wife.

We then launched a Facebook and email survey and sent it to the practice's existing patients, asking a simple question:

"Which color scheme should we use in the NEW office?"

By doing this, we put an effective co-creating mentality in the minds of the patients while announcing the opening of the new office.

The doctor and the staff adore their patients and value their opinions. Now, by involving the patients in the process, they'll get the votes from the people who will be cared for in the new practice, *and* they'll activate the co-creating commitment from them.

As a beautiful byproduct of this event, the practice earned a tremendous amount of activity on Facebook, becoming the talk of the town online in their patient communities. This will inevitably lead to opportunities for people in the community to hear more about the practice from existing patients online, giving the doctor a chance at winning over more new patients. Imagine all the possibilities of patient engagement, trust, and commitment you can earn during a period like this.

Engage your patients, get their input, earn their commitment, build loyalty, and increase new patients.

It's the best of all worlds and everyone wins.

With tools like these, we're able to offset some of the negative effects of a lower PDR during a practice relocation project. The practice is now thriving and having record months.

In short, if you're undergoing a relocation project, the PDR must be prioritized if you hope to pursue future growth. If the PDR is too low, there are additional tools that can be used, but they must be implemented strategically to prevent loss of existing patients and a lower growth rate of new patients.

PDR Misunderstanding #2

"A high PDR is the sole factor in choosing your practice location."

You could lose everything if you rely too heavily on the PDR.

How is this possible?

Many doctors ask us, "Isn't the PDR the most important aspect of the practice's location?"

The answer is yes and no.

One client in Texas asked us to help them analyze areas in the high-growth Maryland suburban areas.

We've worked with doctors who moved from the north to the south, others who are moving from the east coast to the west coast, and even one who wanted to move from Alaska to the Midwest. This particular doctor in Texas was ready to move his family closer to friends and family in Maryland.

Often times, doctors will read some of our publications and do homework on a region before we speak. In some cases, they'll buy this book and then take one of our online demographics training courses to learn how to run all the demographics reports on their own.

In this case, the doctor and his wife did some homework and found a few regions they really liked in Maryland. As a matter of fact, they even found an area with a PDR of 2,729. Rising above the 2,000 benchmark looked good at first glance. But for you, this might not be an area you would want to consider for your practice.

Why?

Do you aspire to have a practice flooded with a Medicaid population?

With a number of our tools and government data, we were able to determine that more than half the population in that specific region had a high likelihood of being Medicaid recipients.

The doctor was shocked—and thankful—that we were able to show them the information they may not have noticed before signing their lease.

For some, a population like the one in that Maryland region fits their vision and their goals. For others, they don't want to base their career on Medicaid patients and will use the tools and the PDR to look further in other regions.

The point of discussing this is to illustrate that the PDR, even when at a healthy level of 2,729, may not be inherently good news.

Each practice location search is unique and has individual needs; full consideration for your vision and goals for your practice is of paramount importance. While an area replete with Medicaid patients is great for some doctors, it's not the right path for others.

PDR MISUNDERSTANDING #3

"I'm doomed if I don't have a high PDR."

The last misunderstanding of the PDR is that all doctors absolutely must have a PDR of at least 2,000 to succeed.

In some rare occasions, a low PDR is rightfully trumped by another factor.

My firm prioritizes the PDR and recommends this as *one* of the higher pieces of first-consideration data. However, there are cases when a location is chosen even with a low PDR.

When might it be okay to open a new office in a region with a low PDR?

Here are two general occasions when we've seen a low PDR found to be acceptable to the doctor:

1. When the region is more important to you than new patient flow

2. When you have a marketing budget and plan prepared to counteract the low PDR

WHEN REGION TRUMPS PDR

A doctor and I once had a conversation about his future in southern California. In his town, the PDR was an abysmally low 820. But in his personal life, his family goals had him committed permanently to that area. Admirably, living near his wife's family was their top priority. Dozens of those family members lived in the town, which meant exploring locations more than 20 minutes away was out of the question.

In cases like these, your family and your life goals are far more important than new-patient flow. While the PDR will unquestionably affect his future new-patient growth, personal goals must be in alignment with Practice Location efforts. For some doctors, the choice of region may trump PDR, even when it will knowingly hamper new patient growth.

WHEN MARKETING PLANS TRUMP PDR

In the Pennsylvania area, a doctor had a six-figure budget for marketing expenses. The concept had been proven on the west coast, he said, and he was convinced it would be effective in his new city. He chose a town with a low PDR, just outside the city limits, and put his idea to the test.

Most start-up practice clients build their business plan to include a marketing budget of $20,000–$40,000, depending on the goals, the vision, and the demographics. We help negotiate that budget as part of your loan with the banks and the results work very well. Our target number of new patients for start-up practices is 40–80 new patients per month, per doctor for most practices. For existing practices, or for start-ups that reach a level of business maturation, it's possible to decrease that budget if the need for new patients decreases.

But for this doctor in Pennsylvania, a full blown TV, radio, and mailing campaign was supposedly the answer. While the practice is still open, however, it rarely looks busy and frequently turns over staff. While the region sees his name all over the local media, his facility has the appearance of a less popular presence.

Marketing for new patients can be a bit like fishing. By spending money on marketing, you're throwing your rod in the water. If you can statistically prove that some ponds don't have the fish you like or enough fish for you and all the other fishermen, spending time there won't be very productive. It may be possible to catch enough fish there, but you'll either need many more rods or several more days. But if you can find a pond known for an abundance of fish, in an area you love, it would be wise to spend time nowhere but in that pond of abundance until you have enough fish in the boat.

For doctors who want a healthy new-patient flow and have their minds set on a region with a low PDR, we strongly recommend budgeting for a large, ambitious, ongoing marketing plan. Multiple rods and lots of days may be the only way out of that pond.

PUTTING IT INTO PRACTICE:

YOUR NEXT STEPS

❖ Looks can be deceiving—choose your best town demographics, not gut feeling or image. Demographics are the key to long-term chances of practice growth.

❖ Make your analysis simple and have the ability to sift through thousands of demographic data points; focus on the 12 demographics criteria that matter most to dentists.

❖ Decide what kind of patient population you want to target. Be honest with yourself. Your long-term, chair-side satisfaction depends on your knowing the population and choosing a demographically supported location to match that decision.

❖ Never underestimate the all-important ratio! 2000:1 is the lowest permissible.

LOCATION DECISION TOOL #2:

THE ONE LEGAL DECISION AFFECTING YOU RIGHT NOW

The word *legal* often sends chills up the spines of my dentist clients because it means one of three things:

- ❖ a lawsuit
- ❖ a legal bill
- ❖ a headache

Thankfully, the "legal" topic we're about to discuss is quite a bit less intense and much easier to think through in a stress-free way.

There are dozens of important legal topics to consider when planning your new practice (legal entity, legal liability, contract review, and more), but the topic at hand is much easier to digest and has a lot of upside for you and your new location.

The legal topic I'm referring to is the one of your **non-compete contract**.

Please note that this portion of our discussion is directed toward the doctors looking to start a new practice as opposed to the doctors looking to move an existing practice.

Why in the world would we discuss your non-compete contract when this is a book about your new office?

One of the most overlooked items in the process of your Location Decision is your current non-compete contract, and it's very often missed at the wrong time. The majority of associates will examine their non-compete (assuming you filed away a copy) while they're working for the senior doctor, close to the time they want to build their own practice. However, ideally, I like to suggest first-year associates strategically only consider associateship positions 10+ miles from their ideal location.

Why do I suggest that?

Because the majority of non-compete contracts have a 5–10 mile radius in which you're disallowed to practice dentistry for a certain period of time following your employment.

For example, if your dream is to someday build in Palmyra, NJ, I might suggest taking an associateship just across the river in Abington, PA, for a few years. But if you're already working in an associateship position, you need to make sure you fully understand your non-compete clause in your employment contract. Not doing this the right way could be crushing and set you back many tens of thousands of dollars—and it's happened on multiple occasions to the loss of the associate.

What if you don't have a copy of the agreement?

Strangely, my first recommendation is *not* to ask your employer for a copy. Most employers are smart enough to know what a request like that implies. Why else might you be looking to review your non-compete contract other than to see if you may be in a place to compete with the senior doctor?

The risk to you as the associate is that most associateship contracts give the employer full authority to terminate the contract and your employment as they see fit. So by asking for a copy, you may inadvertently initiate your own walking papers. Sometimes there's a mutually agreed upon timeframe of notice required of the employer, but either way, it's quite likely that the senior doctor will begin considering a replacement if you ask for a copy of that contract.

There's a small chance that you don't have a non-compete contract, but even one related sentence in any agreement that you could have signed on your overwhelming, butterflies-in-the-stomach first day on the job would hold up in court as a potential conflict against you. And frankly, the employer should be able to limit their exposure to associates who attempt to open an office too close to their practice.

In most situations, the senior doctor is generous with their time, expertise, friendship, trust, and investment. It costs quite a bit to keep an associate busy, happy, and paid on time with all the other demands on the senior doctor's time and resources. So if you're unable to find a copy, it's wise to assume you have some version of a non-compete contract.

Generally speaking, non-compete contracts hold up in court when there's foul play and an associate doctor intentionally lures away existing patients to their new practice. While moving down the street from your old employer may seem like an opportunity to get a jumpstart on building your practice, I highly advise against it.

First, it's effectively stealing and beneath the quality, integrity, and legacy of our community. It is, in fact, the owner-doctor's investment in his practice, team, and reputation that allowed those patients to meet you initially.

Second, the owner-doctor generally provides substantial energy and resources into an associate's time at their office, which should be recognized. While many associates may feel otherwise, employing an associate is an investment, a risk, and requires quite a bit of effort from the owner-doctor than some realize.

It's for all of those reasons that the majority of non-compete clauses in employment contracts have a radius of miles that you must not work within upon departure from your employment there. Typically, the radius is five miles, though I've seen contracts with ten and fifteen miles as well.

Because of all the non-compete elements we just covered, I hope you're reading this book *before* you start working as an associate. If you know anyone considering a new associate position, please share this with them! By considering this Location Decision tool, you'll be able to make sure you're far enough away from your future ideal town.

At this point in our discussion on the Location Decision, you already have the tools needed to study the demographics, and now you know that you should only take an associateship 5–10 miles from that ideal town in preparation for your future. It may feel like a long timeframe between the first day on the job and your new practice's opening day, but I assure you the work and planning you put in now will reward you well for years to come.

As a final note, I feel it important to mention a cruel and unusual tactic I'm beginning to see with some multi-location group practices out there that we need to address. In some of those group practices, the non-compete contract excludes you from working within ten miles of ANY practice in their group. This applies even if you only worked in one of their further locations. Consider that for a moment. If they have eight locations scattered around the town and the surrounding counties, you may have to leave the entire geography that you've come to know and love. Forget the pain of a five-mile non-compete contract; the pain of these less-than-fair group practice non-compete contracts can quickly balloon to a 50-mile radius!

Please know your contracts and look for all possibilities that may conflict with your future vision.

For those who have (or think they have) a non-compete contract and are currently employed but can't locate the radius of miles from the current practice, I would advise you to speak with an attorney familiar with the laws in your state who can guide you on strategy that will work. The shadow of a former employer with the possibility of legal action lingering is not one you should need to be concerned with in your new practice. There will be plenty of duties and responsibilities that are far more important to your success.

Now that you've prepared your thoughts, your map, and your compass delineating a 5–10 mile radius, we'll discuss some further strategies.

PUTTING IT INTO PRACTICE:

Your Next Steps

❖   Don't diminish all the legal issues at hand with your new
    practice.

❖   Relative to your Location Decision, it is essential to review your
    Non-Compete contract.

❖   Don't ask your employer for a copy. Their priority is to care well
    for their patients, and the flight risk of an associate is not good
    for their practice.

❖   Share this information with colleagues BEFORE they take
    another job!

❖   Beware the group practice Non-Compete.

LOCATION DECISION TOOL #3:

OTHER START-UPS

A couple of years ago, I was visiting one of the attractive local towns and I noticed a new dental office being built. It's not terribly uncommon, really, and you've probably seen new dental offices being built too. But in this case, there was more to the story.

If you were the one slowly driving on that particular sunny day through the quaint downtown streets of the borough, you may have noticed one of the "coming soon" signs outside—or maybe the practice name on the marquee caught your eye as you found it an interesting decision to put their signs up before opening day.

As you drove past that office, you may have had the analyst in you try to look a little closer to see what the construction team and the doctor were doing well and what you would change. Then, as traffic began moving again, you imagined what your future practice would look like. In your new office, maybe you'd change something on the outside or look for a different quality of building. Maybe you'd have the feeling of wishing it was you who was opening in that part of town. But if you knew what I knew about *that* borough, on *that* drive, on *that* day, you would have had one prominent overpowering thought: relief.

Why? Because it *wasn't* you opening that practice. If you knew what I knew about that borough, you would never consider *that* borough in the first place. Here is what was happening in the local dental community there:

* ❖ The Population-to-Doctor ratio was unacceptable at 1800:1.

* ❖ A second new practice on the other side of town was being built and would be completed in the same month.

* ❖ Just one week prior, I heard that a third dentist just signed a lease for the real estate of what used to be an oral surgeon's practice.

While all that new access to care is exciting for the local community and the advancement of dentistry, it's not so exciting for those three new practice owners. That increased level of competition for an already limited-potential patient base could be debilitating for a new practice. But I doubt they'll recognize the negative aspects of their situation until they've been moved in for at least three or four years. That's when they may start to agonize over new patient acquisition.

Around the time you think through all of this is when you would sigh with relief on your drive toward your future location, full of knowledge and confidence in your decision.

Even if you're not completely concerned or convinced about this topic, it would be good for you to know that most new practice owners will send out large volumes of marketing. For better or for worse, the "mature" practices rarely send out marketing pieces like postcards and mailers, which leaves a great opportunity for a new practice *if* it's the only start-up practice in that area.

So, one could say that, in general, older practices don't market heavily whereas start-up practices market aggressively. Consider what that would mean if multiple practices are starting up simultaneously. The byproduct of all that simultaneous marketing is that potential patients could feel bombarded by dental marketing and reach a point where they won't respond to dental ads for treatment beyond emergencies. It's called the marketing saturation point. The easiest way to make sure this doesn't happen to you is to work closely with your Practice Project Team, who has a deep understanding of these issues. Their knowledge and local connections will have the inside track on the future plans for your local dental community.

Another strong resource is a relationship with the people in the local township building where you're hoping to build. If you build that relationship well and talk about commercial projects that are underway, they'll almost always share great public information that's difficult to unearth on your own. The local township building holds a record of all the projects (dental or not) that have been applied for and approved. If you can get a peek at the near-future competition of other start-ups, you'll be in a MUCH better position when you start.

Next time you're on a long drive and you see a new practice being built, know that your future will be wrapped in preparation and awareness. You'll make sure you're positioned for the best success and be able to stand out as a premier new dental practice that the community has been waiting for.

PUTTING IT INTO PRACTICE:
YOUR NEXT STEPS

✤   Avoid towns with multiple new practices.

✤   Watch for evidence of new practices in the local mailboxes when you see lots of marketing.

✤   Uncover towns with new practices by speaking with your Practice Project Team—the right team will know.

✤   Communicate with the local municipal building employees to learn about pending projects.

LOCATION DECISION TOOL #4:

THE "AGE OPPORTUNITY"

This is different from the information in the demographics report we discussed above. It's also not at all related to your personal age; rather it refers to the age of the *other* doctors in that area.

Why? **Acquisition Opportunity.**

Some of the most vibrant, thriving practices I've worked with came to be that way through positioning themselves as the acquirer of other practices in their area. In today's booming dental world, it can be complicated and competitive when looking to purchase the goodwill associated with a "patient-charts acquisition," but it can create outstanding results for you.

First, I should point out that in most states, you can't actually purchase patient charts. Technically, you have the ability to purchase goodwill that is associated with specific charts as it is the patients who most own their clinical information. The doctor is solely the maintainer of those patient records and therefore cannot sell them. But a doctor can work with an attorney to create a sale agreement that will enable them to sell the connected goodwill. With that understanding, in this conversation, if we mention the sale of patient records, it is within this framework.

Let's consider the types of charts that are normally available for sale. There are a couple of anomalies we won't spend much time on, but they're interesting to mention. The third situation is the most likely and common.

TRUE STORY #1: BAD PRESS

A doctor with a spending problem had a confrontation with the repo man who came to take away his Jeep Cherokee. In addition to money problems, this individual apparently had anger problems, and the repo man ended up in the hospital after a tire iron caused trauma to his face. After the police came and the trial ended, that doctor ended up in jail, bankrupt. His practice records subsequently went up for sale. The practice, as an entity, never went up for sale, however; I imagine no one wanted to occupy the office space of a criminal, broke dentist. In a situation like this, it's a records-only sale.

TRUE STORY #2: MOTIVATION IS LOW AND SLOW

A doctor died after a long, sad battle with cancer. His family was financially taken care of regardless of the sale of the practice, so the sick doctor continued to practice on the days when he felt well enough. The practice value dwindled as patients knew the situation and production dropped significantly. A couple of years later, after his funeral, the family chose to sell the patient records. The lease was about to expire on the third-floor office building, so they sold off the equipment and chose an "heir" to the patient base who purchased it from the estate. In a situation where an estate is the seller and the motivation to sell quickly is low, a records-only sale is most likely.

THE LIKELY RECORDS-ONLY SALE

A doctor who has had decades of loyalty, success, and professional satisfaction is ready to retire. The golf course and vacation home are calling and he has met his goal, anxious to move on. Like in so many of these situations, the doctor has allowed his practice value to decline, pursuing a relaxed approach to his favorite procedures and patients. Many of the patients have aged with him, marketing has been non-existent, young new patients have been attracted elsewhere, and a large portion of the historic patient base has already passed.

A doctor like this is looking for the right successor who will carry his mantle and represent his legacy well. Very often, his situation implies that the physical practice and the lease status are both undesirable; otherwise, there are few additional reasons why the doctor would be selling only the patient records. With all the technological advancement of the last decade, it becomes complicated for a doctor like this one nearing retirement to keep up, and he knows his facility is less than ideal for a younger, more ambitious doctor-buyer.

This could be an opportunity for you to get a good price on patient records of retiring doctors.

· · ·

One of our clients who recently built her new practice in a small town took this concept to a new level by building a professional relationship with one of the oldest and most likely to retire doctors in the town *before she even started construction*. Brilliant! She now has an agreement in place to have the first right of refusal on the purchase of the patient records when it comes time for the senior doctor to sell. This example is both a great way to build a relationship with local colleagues and a smart way to position your practice for future growth.

• • •

A different client asked us to build his new practice that he purchased six years prior. His current facility could no longer handle his current level of patients and his lease was coming to an end. He was also outgrowing his space quickly. Here is the story of his growth path.

> He started his experience of practice ownership in a high-income town outside of Philadelphia and intentionally made two fortuitous decisions:
>
> ❖ First, he gave himself a goal to acquire three practices as a growth strategy to build up his total number of patients.
>
> ❖ Second, he chose an area with an abundance of doctors of higher age. His town was a stable, albeit non-growing area that had an acceptable Population-to-Doctor ratio. But he knew a few "pops" of patient growth would be needed to move the practice to his desired level of production.
>
> In five years, he had acquired three practices' records and his practice had surpassed his expectations. The research he completed years prior had positioned him perfectly to help the retiring doctors have a strong succession plan, and his practice grew well as a result.

The structure of these kinds of acquisitions normally falls into one of two categories:

1. OUTRIGHT PURCHASE

Buyer and seller will agree to a price, consummate the transaction, and then oftentimes the seller will make his reputation and services available for a certain amount of time to assist in the transition of patients.

2. PAY PER PRODUCTION

Buyer and seller will agree on a percentage of production to pay the selling doctor on *future* production. This will normally occur in tiered percentages and will pay the selling doctor for 2–5 years after the sale.

One example of the percentage of production paid by the buying doctor would be 30% in the first year, 20% in the second, and 10% in the third, paid quarterly under review of an agreed upon accountant or attorney.

For all of these reasons (outside of tire irons and early death), it could be a smart move to choose a location that has a much older doctor community, hence the "Age Opportunity" naming of this chapter. Often I'll share resources with clients that give them the average age of doctors in their area. If you can get some good information on the approximate age of the doctors in your ideal town, you could be in a great spot to acquire patient records in future years, providing a healthy practice growth stream for you and your long-term success.

PUTTING IT INTO PRACTICE:

YOUR NEXT STEPS

❖ Consider gathering data from your Practice Project Team on the ages of local doctors.

❖ Watch for the motivation of the selling doctors to determine if a records sale is possible.

❖ Two kinds of records-only sales are likely: Outright Purchase and Pay Per Production—these are the "Pops" in new patients that could create amazing growth for you!

LOCATION DECISION TOOL #5:

LOCAL MARKET CONCERNS

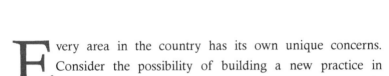

E very area in the country has its own unique concerns. Consider the possibility of building a new practice in Detroit. Now consider building a new practice in Beverly Hills. Differing economies present differing issues. While one area may have a very low cost of living or of doing business, it may also have some immovable, macro-economic explanations that you might be wise to stay away from.

On the other end of the spectrum, a higher income area may be more flash than cash—or perhaps more prestige than income opportunity. But the point of those two extreme examples is the inescapable truth that each local community has its own strengths and weaknesses, pros and cons. Ultimately, there are a few precise differences related to local market concerns that should be considered in every new office project.

In this chapter, we'll discuss how each of the following topics is unique to its local market:

- ❖ Starting with some valuable construction considerations, we'll look at a realistic savings of $50,000 in construction costs.

- ❖ Then we'll touch on a million dollar tax benefit available to you via location selection.

- ❖ The next topic may have the greatest impact in this chapter and deals with "the other side of the tracks."

- ❖ We'll finish with some thoughts on the power of google from a patient's perspective.

These are a few of the most high-impact local market concerns related to your location selection that you need to consider before making your final decision.

The first of the Local Market Concerns is the **cost of construction**. This topic will be brief but could save you $50,000 in the first year of your new practice.

The city of Philadelphia has a population of about 1.5 million residents and therefore plenty of room for dentists to find opportunity. But did you know that in a city like Philadelphia, you'll pay 10–50% *more* in construction costs?

Because of increased fees, taxes, and union effects on prices, a typical new office of 2,000 square feet would cost you approximately $280,000 inside the city limits; whereas, if you shifted your location search to Delaware, New Jersey, or the Philadelphia suburbs, the cost for the same practice construction would cost you $200,000–$230,000. That's a $50,000–$80,000 construction cost difference.

With a short drive into any of the surrounding areas, you could save enough to pay for the down payment on your next home. It's best to speak with your Practice Project Team and learn about any gaping disparities in construction costs to eliminate large areas from your search.

Now, let's look at the related of **tax rates**.

Snore. Yes, taxes may bore most of us and even seem out of place in this conversation, but they're poignant financial land mines lying quietly in the topic of local market concerns.

The other reason local taxes shouldn't bore you is the reality of leaving $1 million unearned. Are you awake now? There are plenty of tax and accounting professionals who could deliver you the most relevant information for the local market, so consult with them. But for the purposes of this conversation, allow me to mention *local* tax rates.

Some municipalities, townships, and boroughs will charge a flat percentage on gross receipts, others on personal income, and others none at all. Since we're in a pattern of pointing out concerns with Philadelphia in this chapter, we'll mention one of their taxes as an example.

In Philadelphia, the city has a tax on all wages earned within the city limits at a rate between 3.49% and 3.9%. For the average dentist's income level, that will decrease your personal take-home pay by nearly $10,000 every single year. $10,000 per year sounds like a lot, but I'd like to put it in a more dramatic perspective for you:

If you save $10,000 every year for 30 years and earn a return of 6%, you will have saved more than $1,000,000.

That sounds like a good reason to consider local tax rates before finalizing your new practice location decision. Each area has its own tax issues, but I recommend you weigh those as part of your long-term planning and location decision process. It might make the difference in your freedom to choose your retirement age.

The next Local Market Concern you will benefit from is **local perception**.

Now, if you grew up in the town where you plan on locating your new office, this section does not apply to you. However, if you didn't grow up from childhood in your future office's town, this next paragraph will save you the unfortunate pain of major regret and loads of unneeded effort from you and your staff to attract new patients. How can that be?

Local Perception refers to the colloquialism, "the wrong side of the tracks." We've all heard that phrase before, and it's usually used in a sentence like this one:

> "He had such a hard life. You know he grew up on the wrong side of the tracks, don't you?"

Let's be candid here and point out that there aren't railroad tracks in any town in America that are a physical boundary between happiness and unhappiness. People are far too able to change their path in life here in the United States for a mythical set of steel beams to affect their future. However, the "wrong side of the tracks" represents a real and accurate *perception* in most towns. That perception is one related to prestige, stable home life, opportunity, income, and status.

Regardless of the patient population you hope to serve, it will almost always benefit you and your practice's future to locate your office on *this* side of *those* tracks, where perception places you on the more desirable side, and where you will attract more patients. The alternative is to place your practice on the wrong side of the tracks where a portion of the local population who has greater aspirations for their life and health won't visit. Human nature is to reach upward.

One of my favorite quotes is by a man named Leo Burnett who said it best.

"When you reach for the stars, you may not quite get one, but you won't come up with a handful of mud either."

Leo's quote points to our ability and propensity to aim higher and reach for greater potential, which is a natural driving force in all of us. If your practice is on the better side of those tracks, you'll be positioning it closer to the stars than the mud. As an excellent clinician, you'll offer superior care to all people from any part of the town, but don't let your practice get stuck trying to work against that driving force of patients wanting to visit a practice that isn't yours.

The most important part of this piece of our discussion is the nature of the tracks being invisible to you—the person who didn't spend a lifetime living there—understanding all the nuances of the tracks. Without a local history, you'll never know where the tracks are located. Of course, it's easy to find the nicer shops, the nicer homes, and the nicer streets in a town, but the question you need to be very clear about is, "Where do the tracks separate the nicer things in the town?" The geographical distance can be as little as a few feet, but the local community and their perceptions decide these rules, which don't have profit-related consequences.

What is the simplest way to figure out the location of these invisible tracks in your future town?

Since you didn't spend your childhood there, and you don't know where they are, you should ask a police officer. I'm serious. One of the local law enforcement professionals will be able to tell you without hesitation which areas are on the other side of the tracks. One conversation like this could open up potential for a new patient flow that may never be accomplished or attracted if you position your practice on the wrong side. Choose your side wisely, and let natural human attraction to the more desirable things work in your favor. As a result, you'll attract people from the entire town, expanding your ability to offer great clinical care to more people.

The last topic in our conversation about Local Market Concerns for your new practice is about **Google** and **Apple**.

Specifically, we're talking about their maps. If you look at people's cell phones today, it seems nine out of ten are smartphones—and smartphones are mobile GPS devices. In your new practice, you'll need to compel numerous people to your office and make it easy for them to find you. For this reason, it's crucial that your new address is locatable in both Google and Apple maps, because any degree of frustration or confusion can prevent a new patient from coming to their first appointment.

For more precise dentist-specific instructions on registering your practice location with Google and Apple maps, please visit our blog and enter "maps" in the search box.

www.HowToOpenADentalOffice.com/blog

Just imagine how many reluctant spouses who finally agree to "get their teeth cleaned" would be more than happy to not find your practice? Prevent no-shows, make it easier to find your practice, and increase new patient flow by making sure your address shows up in both of those mapping apps, and then register your address with them. Doing so will literally put your practice on the map, and you'll meet the expectations of patients that your practice is easy to find (and then that spouse will have to come up with a different excuse!).

PUTTING IT INTO PRACTICE:

YOUR NEXT STEPS

❖ Save $50,000 (truly!) by building outside of the wrong area.

❖ Examine local tax rates—mid-range local taxes can quickly swipe $1,000,000 from your retirement.

❖ Discuss "the tracks" with the local community to avoid being on the wrong side.

❖ Search our blog for "maps" and get directions to have your practice listed—don't let a patient "accidentally" miss their appointment!

LOCATION DECISION TOOL #6:

OFFICE LEASE –
THE OVERLOOKED DANGER

———◆———

The age-old question of "lease versus own" embodies one of the largest portions of our economy, one of the most significant for your future, and one of the most defining of your personal financial situation.

Many would say you should have a strong opinion on the topic of owning your business property before you open your new practice. To be candid, I disagree with the notion that there is a firm, correct answer in that situation. There are large, profitable companies like Home Depot, Target, and Walmart who *lease* real estate. Alternatively, there are multimillion dollar franchised businesses that won't consider opening a new location without *owning* the real estate. The answer is not definitive, and for dentists, it typically boils down to personal preference and discussions with your financial advisor.

But that part of the real estate topic is not the driving force of this chapter. Here, we're going to focus on the overlooked danger of an office lease—a danger unique to dentists. The likely career-defining information you'll uncover below will show you the side of the real estate conversation that landlords and property owners don't want you to focus on. We'll leave the analysis of lease versus own to the financial planners and the accountants. For you, the following discussion is the most important real estate topic of all.

I propose that the topics below are important enough to make or break your decision on any location. These are career-shaping thoughts on lease negotiation.

To be clear, I don't want to disappoint you. There is no magic bullet to getting a deal on a lease or purchase. You could probably buy a dozen books on the art of wheeling and dealing in real estate, but I can tell you with first-hand knowledge that you'll likely pay "market rate."

The real power is not in the rate you pay, and the real danger is actually the multitude of overlooked components of a lease that can, individually, be the determining factor between a profitable career and painful one. But first, let's discuss the most attractive and possibly least important piece of the "Market Rate" topic.

Over the millions of dollars of leasing and purchasing I've been involved in for small businesses who need 1,000–5,000 square feet of space, market rates generally prevail and you will pay a price close to market rate in any healthy real estate market. In the rare occasions where a landlord or seller is in a financially weak position and you have remarkably lucky timing and stellar negotiating skills, you may feel like you're getting a great bargain. But for the vast majority of leases and purchases the size of which dentists will engage in, market rate is what you'll pay after you find the town that has the best criteria for your practice's needs.

So why do people focus on and brag about the deal they got on a lease or a purchase price?

Because the landlords and property owners want you to. This is the key to our discussion in this chapter. Landlords know that everyone feels a little better and bigger when they feel like they've negotiated a good deal, and many landlords count on that occurring. Unfortunately and ironically, an emphasis on price is exactly the wrong thing to be focused on for your long-term goals. Hence, I offer you a glimpse into my multiple experiences as both lessee and lessor, which put a gravely different perspective on the issue.

Like a moth attracted to that purple buzzing light at an evening picnic on a hot summer day, landlords and owners hope you'll stare right into the light of the price and your perceived negotiation victory. Imagine the elation you feel when you "win" with the realtor's help and save $2 per square foot on your ten-year lease. That's a great feeling! Both you and the realtor high five and are compelled to sign it as fast as you can and fax a copy back, seizing thousands of dollars in savings per year.

But the landlord and property owner are thrilled because they got you into the space, with signed paperwork. That paperwork holds dozens and perhaps hundreds of provisions that put immense power in the landlord's hands. They know that you as a dentist are in the industry that requires the largest investment per square foot in the country. With that knowledge, they have immeasurable leverage over you and they know that they have opportunity in the rest of that lease to work circumstances to their favor.

Why do you think there are so many pages to a lease?

The pages are not there to protect anyone but the landlord. What, then, could be in those other pages that can be so detrimental and simultaneously bring a smile to the landlord's face when you "win" the price negotiation?

I've helped many clients negotiate leases to their benefit, and sometimes they've done it while *intentionally* paying a price per square foot exactly equal to what the landlord advertised. There are great reasons to do this and they boil down to the rest of that lease, which is something you need to be aware of. This topic is so important that there are even a few firms with whom I've built deep relationships, and I've subsequently directed those clients to engage in lease negotiations that save hundreds of thousands of dollars over the lifetime of the practice. And, again, the issue at hand is not the price per square foot.

Perhaps the concern of prime importance buried deep in those lease documents is the one that allows for the legal transfer of your practice to a buyer of your choice. Do not take this seemingly inconsequential, distant topic lightly, as those who do may have ruined retirement plans without knowing it. Landlords who have a bug staring at the light of a price negotiation know they're in a strong position, and with any of a dozen variations can include a loophole to their advantage. They may include a provision that subtly allows the landlord to have the sole discretion on who can purchase the practice, and that could easily spell financial disaster for you and a financial windfall for the landlord.

Imagine you've been in the space for 25 years and it's time for you to sell. You find the ideal buyer, prepare to go to the settlement table, and go to the landlord's office to ask for a copy of the lease to bring to closing. What might happen is the landlord who had you sign a lease containing that clause conveniently denies the prospective buyers, claiming their rights in the lease … until the rent is raised 30%. Without a lease, you don't have a practice to sell.

What would you do? It can and has happened. What might happen to the value of your practice and ultimately your sale price of the practice if you're trapped in that situation? You may not even be able to sell at all.

Consider another gut-turning possibility:

The landlord may use creative language, giving him the authority to require you to move to another suite in the building, or worse, to another building. Landlords hire the best attorneys and purposely create confusing and cloaked language to retain the most control. Remember an important fact specific to our dental community: landlords know the extensive and expensive costs of dental construction, and they can use that as leverage for their financial gain. Like monarchs from the dark ages, they're not called Lords of Land for nothing.

In some of my clients' leases, I've even seen an uncommon but fully legal clause in the lease named "confession of judgement," in which the tenant admits guilt for any breach of lease without the opportunity to fight legally. That's another way of saying guilty before any discussion. At first glance, that may sound unfair and simultaneously seem irrelevant. How often are leases breached, anyway?

Consider the term "breach of lease" again. Nearly every lease has a noise clause.

- ❖ Is your compressor going to sound dampened well enough?
- ❖ Or how about the clause that was never enforced about business hours—did the landlord ever send a signed, modified page of the lease, allowing you to practice after normal business hours?

These are all examples of "breaches of lease," and the landlord doesn't necessarily need to alert you to it at the time of infraction. Any one of these, or hundreds of other possibilities, could decimate your financial situation. At any moment, a breach of lease could accelerate the terms of it, commanding the *entire* value of years of the lease to be paid to the landlord immediately on demand. In a situation like that, you pay up or you move out. And the landlord knows you need 6–12 months to open a new practice. What will you do? In a horrible position like that, you have no good options.

Many tenants will tell themselves that their landlord would never pull a stunt like that—and perhaps that's true. But more and more, local commercial landlords are selling to large multinational firms, and we all know that benevolence and generosity aren't the first attributes they offer.

These are true, real examples, and there are hundreds more like these that matter far more than the price per square foot. Landlords can use the power of their lease to influence and control your situation in ways people in non-legal professions can't imagine being true. Does that sound ominous? I hope it does, and I also hope it helps you in your location selection for your new practice.

Your Practice Project Team must be able to offer you resources to focus on this topic beyond a typical legal review of the terms in the lease. Your success, peace of mind, and future options in life can be directly tied to the proper handling of this topic.

In all situations, if a landlord isn't willing to modify a lease in a way that satisfies your goals, you should walk. If, by chance, that's the only building available in the town you've chosen—with all the other criteria in this book, and walking away means leaving the town and starting the search all over again—you still need to walk away. A lease holds immense power over your professional and personal life, and if the lease for your new practice doesn't align perfectly with your goals—not just your desired price per square foot—please walk away and save yourself the future regret and loss.

PUTTING IT INTO PRACTICE:
YOUR NEXT STEPS

❖ Lease versus own is not a simple topic with a clear answer. Explore what fits your long-term goals.

❖ Landlords want you to stay focused on price. Don't let them.

❖ Discuss a proper lease review with a dental-specific firm—the average attorney or realtor will almost always leave the intricate needs of a dental practice vulnerable.

❖ Walk. If the lease doesn't give you protection, find a new building, town, or even state. The wrong lease is not worth it.

LOCATION DECISION TOOL #7:

INSURANCE PARTNERING

———⟨◆⟩———

I n this chapter, you'll discover some of the coveted techniques used to collaborate with insurance companies that will allow you to target the highest reimbursement schedules, and you'll also be one of the few doctors privy to the invaluable opportunities available through partnering with insurance companies. In both of the topics in this chapter, you will be more prepared to find and choose a location that will yield higher profits.

First, let's discuss a painful topic: **insurance reimbursement rates**.

In today's dental economy, the insurance company's reimbursement schedules are increasingly important to your success. I've heard it said that nationwide, 87% of dentistry is PPO driven. Relative to the last 50 years of dentistry, that percentage is stunning and it represents a national shift in the way the business of dentistry is and will forever be conducted.

According to all credible sources on this topic, it seems that dental providers throughout the nation won't move away from insurance participation anytime soon. And here's the powerful information to consider:

Some of my clients write off as much as 45% of their production in the form of reimbursement-level discounts while others, just a few miles away, have insurance company write-offs of just 25%.

Everyone in dentistry is aware of the painfully expensive effects that come with insurance write-offs, but few recognize the existence of such wild fluctuations in reimbursement rates in nearby regions. Assuming you're somewhere on the explorative timeline of opening a practice, the levels of reimbursement by community must be calculated as part of the decision process so you don't end up earning less than you deserve. Know thy reimbursement levels. Better yet, know thy insurance sales representative. We'll discuss this concept briefly below.

What about the significance of this topic for the existing practice, where you're looking to move the office to a new location? Did you know that with a few minor changes to your practice's legal entity structure or location, you may lose your existing reimbursement schedule? In other words, a practice move could be the indirect cause of giving legal permission to the insurance companies to decrease your reimbursement rates! This is the awful, legal truth afforded to the insurance industry via power of lobbyists and attorneys. It's no wonder why some have deemed the insurance companies "legalized mafia."

Please, in your journey toward your new office, have discussions with the insurance companies you participate with and get as much in writing as they will give you. It would be good if they would obligate themselves in writing to maintain your existing fee schedule upon your move or your change in legal entity, but it would be ideal if you used your upcoming changes as an opportunity to negotiate your fees to a higher level. Can it be done? Absolutely, and I've guided multiple clients toward that end.

Frequently, I make professional connections between insurance company sales representatives and the doctor-clients I work with so that they can begin a discussion about reimbursement rates and ideal towns to consider. Additionally, many of my clients have engaged the services of a specific, credible insurance company negotiation firm. In many of these instances, I find it encouraging that the insurance company sales representatives generally work with doctors to find mutually beneficial solutions. They certainly can't match a fee-for-service schedule for your reimbursement levels, but when approaching them with rationale, respect, and professional courtesy, they often work toward satisfying agreements.

> One good example of this is the doctor of a start-up practice who pursued a strategic location selection in tandem with insurance companies. The practice was wonderfully positioned from their opening day to be one of the few providers for that insurance plan in that region. How did that benefit the practice? This brought the doctor's practice higher patient flow, the lifeblood to start-up practice success. The doctor would have never known about the opportunity without the conversation taking place with the insurance company during the planning stages of location selection.

If a doctor can build a strong professional relationship with the insurance companies, they may be able to find which areas have higher levels of reimbursement too. In other words, remember the example I mentioned above with the 45% and 25% reimbursement rate practices? Both are general dentistry practices, have the same number of providers, similar numbers of patients, and for all intents and purposes, very similar practices.

If presented with a choice between those two locations for your new practice, you would obviously choose to build where there are higher reimbursement rates. But to accomplish this, you must know the information to apply the knowledge. It's been said that knowledge is power, but *applied* knowledge matters. If you have relationships with the insurance companies and the knowledge of reimbursement rates for strategic locations ahead of time, you can use that information to make the final decision when choosing between towns.

So remember that there are some prominent dental insurance companies that are actually looking for more providers in very specific regions. If you can work with the insurance companies in your exploration, both sides can win and your ideal practice location will be in a much better financial position in the long run.

A final note on this topic:

Insurance Partnering has been deemed one of the top three profit considerations to be analyzed prior to opening a new office. During an interview with the Academy of Dental Management Consultants, these topics were discussed and explained as our team has seen them work for dentists across the country. As a result of the interview, the dental industry took note and now new offices are experiencing a new level of clarity as they look to open in their new location.

As a free resource, you can listen to the interview here:

www.HowToOpenADentalOffice.com/jayme-interview

PUTTING IT INTO PRACTICE:

YOUR NEXT STEPS

- ❖ Leverage the concept of partnership with insurance companies for massive long-term benefits.

- ❖ The right Practice Project Team will be able to connect you to the local insurance contacts you need.

- ❖ PPOs are a near necessity for all new practice owners—find the path to writing off 25% instead of 45%.

LOCATION DECISION TOOL #8:

REALTORS

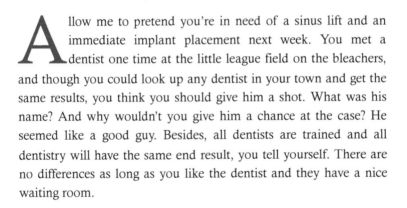

Allow me to pretend you're in need of a sinus lift and an immediate implant placement next week. You met a dentist one time at the little league field on the bleachers, and though you could look up any dentist in your town and get the same results, you think you should give him a shot. What was his name? And why wouldn't you give him a chance at the case? He seemed like a good guy. Besides, all dentists are trained and all dentistry will have the same end result, you tell yourself. There are no differences as long as you like the dentist and they have a nice waiting room.

What?!

I hope you heard the sarcasm dripping over the last paragraph. Of course there are differences in a large case like that. I'm dramatizing the scene and can't imagine you thinking that way, but we should agree that beyond the most detailed of clinical skills needed, there are some important traits you should seek out:

❖ Experience   ❖ Confidence

❖ Exposure   ❖ Empathy

❖ Training   ❖ Education

❖ Intuition   ❖ History

I hope I can convince you that it's the same with realtors.

I would be remiss if we didn't include this topic in our conversation. An overwhelming majority of real estate transactions are completed with the assistance of a realtor, and even in the rare for-sale-by-owner commercial real estate market, realtors will often be asked to advise a portion—or even an entire party's side—of the transaction. In other words, there's a strong chance you'll be working with a realtor when you search for your new practice's home. No surprise, right?

For that reason, the important part of this topic is not "if" you'll use a realtor but "which" realtor you'll have on your team. In multiple places in this book, we mentioned your team, and a realtor is one of the most important members on the front end of your process. This is an opportunity to have an incredible level of experience brought to your team in order to scout, seek out, and filter through real estate options that fit your criteria.

But how many times has the realtor gone through a process like this with a dentist? How could they possibly know all the minutiae of dental office design, optimal room depth, plumbing concerns, best signage, ADA guidelines, water usage tables, and more? They can't without the proper background, just like if you needed an invasive procedure like a sinus lift.

Let's put it another way. Their background does matter. You may have a best friend who recently completed realtor's training and you want to help them earn a commission, or you may have a realtor golfing buddy who has been dropping hints once he heard about your upcoming practice. But the best way to ensure you have a realtor who will help you avoid mental, emotional, and financial loss is to find one with the acute experience and skill related to *your* profession and *your* style of practicing.

Some of my closest friends are realtors, and of all the realtors I've come to respect and trust, there are only two who have the experience I would require if I were a dentist looking for a new practice location. I've found realtors who deeply care for the success and the satisfaction of their "buyers," but their intentions can only bring your practice search the best results if they have the right experience.

Here is our grand finale and the crescendo of the realtor discussion:

There is no room for error at the realtor stage of your project, so consider only working with realtors who have helped at least ten dentists.

Yes, ten. They do exist, but they're rare and when you find yours, you'll understand why a "large case" holds similar implications in real estate to those in dentistry. This is *your* large case, and it should be cared for by the best.

PUTTING IT INTO PRACTICE:

YOUR NEXT STEPS

✤   Not all realtors are created equal!

✤   Get a strong introduction: Your Practice Project Team must be able to make this connection for you.

✤   The right realtor can drastically improve your new practice location search, especially if they know the criteria you've come to understand.

LOCATION DECISION TOOL #9:

THE EMOTIONAL BUILDING

———⟨◆⟩———

Buildings bring out the emotions in everyone. Remember when you moved into your first apartment? Can you recall turning the key in the door the first time? What was the weather like on moving day when you and your spouse chose your first home? What did you do to celebrate the start of your new life? The dreams all started to come together, the unity deepened, and the sense of pride and accomplishment rose to a new level in an experience you'll never forget.

I remember our first dinner of wine and pizza on the tabletop (that had its legs still removed) on the floor of our first home. I don't think we even had a lamp on that first night, but I can still see the memory with perfect clarity. Buildings are emotional.

Being that this final topic is possibly the most emotional of the entire book, will you cry? No. Will you begin to imagine the look and feel of your first dental home? I hope so. This part of the journey is exciting, tangible, memorable,, and a life-defining moment. We should avoid, however, becoming emotionally *convinced.* The exterior style you like so much on the building you may have had your eyes on lately should be one of the last things we use to make this decision.

With all the other criteria we've discussed in this book, I hope you'll agree that there are some topics that should take precedence. Aesthetic value is true value, but I'd like to bring to your attention our final tools so you can thoroughly process through a few of the key components of the ideal building. With some advanced planning placed ahead of the connection you deepen with a building, we can avoid some hurdles and headaches in the long run.

What you won't get in this chapter are typical, easy, page-filling concepts that you can get from anyone who has visited a small business's building. Anyone could rattle off ideas on the best kinds of buildings for your practice, but there are no proven, ironclad theories on the ideal building style for dentistry. Don't believe hype about this topic from opinion makers—they're often not true. However, this chapter as our final has six unique perspectives on building issues that most of my clients say they hadn't considered fully. My hope is that you'll benefit from these in the quest for your perfect practice location.

A. LANDMARK

If you can find a location next to or across from a definable landmark in your town, you and your staff will love the benefits. You don't need to be directly in the shadow of city hall, but you should be located very near an icon in the community. What icons are in your town?

Not only will patients perceive your practice to be more embedded into the community from your opening day, but there is the practical implication of finding your practice. Your staff will have a much simpler task of explaining how to find the practice, and more importantly, patients like going to familiar places—particularly in cases where the purpose of the visit is for a healthcare service (not as exciting as their pending vacation).

With a more familiar landmark positioned near your practice, directions and driving habits will be substantially less stressful for new patients, and that will help your practice create a more complete, enjoyable experience. A practice next to a landmark is one of higher prestige and familiarity, and few would argue that prestige and familiarity are both desirable for your new office.

B. TRAFFIC LIGHT

Every good driver has muttered a foul word at a red light or two, but then you relax and look around. What might you see when you do that?

On the topic of being located at a traffic light or a major intersection, many rightly ask themselves if it's safer for patients to pull out from an exit with a traffic light. Of course it is and that's a good thing, but it's not the best reason for that traffic light. Is it easier to find your practice if you're located at a larger intersection? Absolutely. But could the best reason for being next to a traffic light be drivers staring at your sign *every* time they hit a red light? Bingo.

There are few new patient acquisition strategies better than a traffic light, and with the proper design of your signage, a red light will be your new best friend. One of my clients has been open for three years and has yet to spend more than $1,000 per year on advertising —and she only had 300 patients when she moved to the new location. She now regularly attracts 35 new patients per month (well above the national average of 20), and the culprit of that empowering, profitable, and satisfying number? Her 1/8 mile distance from a major traffic signal and her incredible sign. Some say a picture is worth a thousand words, but I say a sign near a traffic light is worth a thousand patients. So now a word on signs …

C. SIGNAGE

Ah, the over-discussed topic of signs. Everyone has an opinion about which signs are good, but I only know which signs have brought in high levels of new patients. If your sign is going to work for you, it must include certain elements. For this topic, I'm borrowing the post from my blog named, "5 Rules for Great Dental Signs." Be sure to check out the blog for other great ideas at:

www.HowToOpenADentalOffice.com/blog

The most important Dental Office Sign Rule is #5. But make sure you see the examples on pages 79–80, along with the six things you need to include on your next sign.

The 5 Rules for Great Dental Office Signs:

1. GO OUTSIDE

Look at your building and make sure traffic can see your sign clearly. I've seen so many practices that have good signs positioned in a way that hurts more than helps. A great idea I heard once was to get a cheap piece of plywood from Home Depot, spray paint it with your name, position it (or ask a good friend to hold it up), and drive past the building a few times. This is a sign that will last you for many years, so just like a good try-in for a crown, get a good try-in on the sign!

2. FREE AD

Keep in mind that your sign may prevent you from needing to place an ad. Yes, a sign can work that well. Some will even go so far as to make the signage their primary deciding factor on choosing one building over another. Certainly, it depends on your location, but the client I mentioned who consistently gets 35 new patients per month from her sign alone—that keeps her from needing to place an ad. Why?

3. PHONE NUMBER

There are apparently more signs out there without phone numbers than I think reasonable. In an era where people want instant gratification, how much better is it to aid them with that? Help them call you on their drive by putting your phone number LARGE on your sign. Don't assume they'll go home, remember your clever name, write down the number, take it to work, and then call you on their lunch break. Help people satisfy their desire to get things now and they'll call. No phone number, no phone call.

4. WEBSITE

Consider re-reading #3 and replace "phone number" with "website." Now remember that most phones are smartphones!

5. BORING

Yes, I'm suggesting you be boring with your sign. Most marketing tries really hard, but it often boasts the virtues of the business, not the benefit for the customer.

Did I just say don't let your sign say much? Yes, I did.

For example, if your sign has the four types of dentistry on it that you want to be known for, along with your phone number, slogan, website, logo, name, special color scheme, and practice name, you better have a billboard, not a sign. So by boring, what I mean is that while the virtues of your practice are important, they really shouldn't be on your sign. If you have enough space, here's what I've seen yield the highest new patient results—and the following order is specifically how I would prioritize the information on your sign:

- ❖ The word "Dentist" or "Dental" as the first or second word of three maximum words on the first "line" of your sign

- ❖ A white background with dark colored letters—it's been proven that it's easier for the eye to read (think paper in a book), and since we're hoping people can read your sign, you get the idea.

- ❖ Your name, which is required in most states

- ❖ Phone number

- ❖ Website

- ❖ "Accepting new patients" as a possible flag or giant sticker of a bright color

- ❖ Address, if required

Dental signs across the country all have varying degrees of success, but the elements needed for an effective sign are the same anywhere in the country. Let your sign speak the simplest of information to accomplish what you most want: awareness and new patients.

Here's to you and your new sign!

Good Examples found on Google:

Dare I call the good ones boring? In a good way, I think I might!

Not so much in love with these examples:

dark background, big logo, no phone number,
no website

dark background, no website, no phone number,
far too many words, clever but not effective

logo hurting more than helping, no phone number, no website, dark background

name, white background, phone number—boring, but great!

D. HOSPITAL VALUE

A couple of our clients have chosen to start their practices in hospital-campus buildings. While they may not be able to build directly in the hospital because of various regulations, they chose to pay a significantly higher rate for a space on the hospital campus instead of paying a lower rate down the street. While I only have a couple of examples of this from my own experience, I can tell you it seems to have a tremendous effect on new patient flow.

The more recent of the two practices does very little advertising and sees 75 new patients per month. The older of the two practices has far more patients than he can fit in his schedule. While my firm opinion on the topic of Hospital Value is yet to be concluded, I recommend every client consider the option and see if there is room for a clinically excellent dentist on the campus. It could provide you with the prestige of working on a medical campus and the most productive new patient flow amongst your colleagues.

E. PARKING

Believe it or not, patients will need to park their cars. Staff too. Sometimes, parking is one of the last concerns for a small business owner, but its importance from a practical and financial perspective shouldn't be overlooked. I don't know about you, but I have avoided certain retail centers if I know the parking is bad. This is particularly important with practices who hope to attract families with children. There aren't too many moms who want to walk their four kids across a busy road to get to the dentist.

In addition to the practical aspect of needing parking spaces, most towns will require a set number of parking spots per operatory, usually 3–4. If your choice location doesn't meet the requirement, your practice can't get local approvals for use until you invest in creating the additional parking spaces, and that can be quite an expensive investment. If you don't want to make the investment in an expensive parking lot, along with the civil engineering studies and hardscaping required for water runoff, you'll need to take the issue to the local planning and development committee in the town.

Some may enjoy the time and expense of working with a committee like that, but most dentists I work with prefer opening their practice and getting chair-side. This topic will be unavoidable in the planning process of your space while you're working through building permit issues, but it's a budget-busting topic if you don't know this prior to committing to your location and budget. Try to look into the topic of parking with the town you're targeting ahead of time, and you may save yourself the time of looking at locations that don't qualify.

F. CURB APPEAL

The power of a nice building is nearly unbelievable. How do I know? I once was competing to lease a space for a client with Starbucks. The choices in that town were very limited because of some rapid population growth and lagging construction development, and there were only two buildings of similar square footage available in the part of town where we wanted to have the new office.

Starbucks apparently had the same requirements as my client and we lost the fight. They up-bid the price of the lease by $4 per square foot! As a result, my client is saving nearly $8 total per square foot compared to what Starbucks is paying. But as I examine what criteria Starbucks must have used in their Location Decision, I imagine only one topic allowed their uber business-savvy minds to pay such a premium: Curb appeal.

And, what might you ask, was the alternative?

A building of similar everything … *except* curb appeal. Image matters. The exterior of a building is closely associated with the perceived quality of the business inside—for better or worse. Every practice budget has a threshold, but a modest increase in the budget for a similar building with better curb appeal could create drastically greater results for your practice success.

There's a reason I held the topic of Curb Appeal for last. Why, might you ask?

Because on our list of nine tools, twelve demographic concerns, and six thoughts on The Building, the façade of a facility is arguably the easiest of all criteria to assess. As a result, the façade is normally the first that gets the attention of the tenant. I'm confident you'll know if a building looks "good" versus "bad" in all of fifteen seconds. What I mean is that you're certainly fully qualified to find a decent-looking facility, but the danger is that the curb appeal may unjustly influence and decrease your reliance on all the other important topics in this book.

Your focus on the criteria we've discussed is imperative to your long-term success, and they command your attention even if you can't see those criteria as clearly as a façade.

We've mentioned earlier in our discussion that there are hundreds of thousands of dollars at stake in this project and that the Location Decision may be the defining moment in your career. Your emotional strength, your investment in your education, your ability to provide for your family, and your chance at creating a powerful legacy will all be correlated with your location.

While curb appeal is undeniably important in your Location Decision, it is just one of numerous factors in that decision. So savor the gratifying process of making the final curb appeal decision while granting it a balanced perspective against the other criteria we've evaluated.

PUTTING IT INTO PRACTICE:

YOUR NEXT STEPS

❖ Create an emotionally un-charged search process with these tools. There will be plenty of years to fully experience the gamut of emotions, but your location decision cannot be jeopardized by non-subjective criteria. These tools will make it a bit easier to have a guide for that process.

❖ Be a patient, with patient's eyes. Is it easy to find the location? Do you feel comfortable? Is it recognizable and memorable?

❖ In short, your location should not require a patient to think. Find a location that requires as little thought as possible to find.

CONCLUSION

As we finish up here, I'd like to ask you to celebrate. You've just completed a look into some of the defining factors that will help increase your chances of success, fulfillment, and pride in your new practice. You're closer now than you've ever been, and you're far ahead of where you were when you started this journey. Now it's time to take the next steps. Be bold and confident!

It's possible that you may not find a facility that reaches 100% perfection in each of the criterion we've discussed, but my hope is that with the direction of these nine tools, you and others in our dental community will dramatically reduce the pain, frustrations, risks, and costs of unintentionally stepping into the wrong location.

The complete process of your Location Decision will not be without surprises and the path may not feel easy, but the "difficulty" of this process for you is not negative; rather, it is your chance to push through a complex and challenging topic with the product of your hard work leading to enthusiasm, a deepened passion for your daily clinical activities, and most importantly, an amazing end result in your new facility.

Imagine the sense of accomplishment you'll feel as you walk in the front door on your first day. Envision the impressed look in patients' eyes as they take their first tour in your new treatment area. Consider the earned pride you'll feel as people in the community recognize your name as the one with the thriving new practice.

Those will be the transformational moments that make all the effort worth it.

After working with hundreds of your colleagues, I feel I have a strong assumption about why you're here on this page, completing this process of considering your Location Decision. I believe you're here because you have deep within you a restlessness that is pushing you toward something better, and you know it's within your reach.

Perhaps you're like most of my clients and want to provide the best possible care to your patients, and you know an ideal facility is part of that process. With these tools and the right Practice Project Team, you can enter into this next transformative stage of your career, completely sure you've analyzed all of your options and chosen the best possible path. You will have increased your odds of success and satisfaction well beyond those of your colleagues; your new practice will be your "one giant leap" toward the next level of care you hope to deliver with the fulfillment you know to be possible.

In your hands you have developed and refined a wonderful ability to affect the oral health of your patients, but in addition to that, your hands hold the power to affect the pride, fulfillment, and satisfaction that you'll derive from your facility. This is the next step toward the rest of your career.

I won't rehash what we've covered in the prior chapters because I hope you'll use this book as a powerful reference that you can return to over and over in your location search. Wear out the pages and fill up the margins as you prepare, dream, and plan.

I hope you'll make thorough use of all the additional resources at:

www.HowToOpenADentalOffice.com

Please update us on your transformation, tell us about the pursuit of your new practice, and let us know how we can assist you. My team has delivered outstanding results through on-site visits, site selection, connections with insurance companies, lease review, signage creation, demographics analyses, and financing options. We love helping our clients enhance their experience through their new practice process, and I hope you're soon to be one of the success stories.

While we've discussed nine tools through these pages, I would like to offer one final tool for you to consider … Tool #10.

TOOL #10

ASSEMBLING YOUR
PRACTICE PROJECT TEAM

This entire book deals with *where* to build instead of *how*, but there is a bridge between those two distinctly different topics. That bridge is the Practice Project Team. These will be the people who follow your lead on your Location Decision and carry your vision forward in the physical manifestation of your vision in your new office.

We've mentioned a few of the players on that team through these pages, but I want to assure you of the critical nature of needing the right team in place. Like with all people in life, motives, skills, integrity, and track record vary substantially from person to person, and it will be no different with the people who want to be on your Practice Project Team. Choose them with intense discernment. The following factors cannot permit de facto admission for the members of your team:

❖ The "supply guy" with whom you've had a long relationship

❖ The CPA "everybody else" uses

❖ The realtor who is the best family connection

❖ The attorney who did your last set of legal agreements

❖ The contractor everybody in town knows

❖ The banker who networks with other business owners

Your Practice Project Team needs to be comprised of the best. The bar must be raised high for your new practice because the stakes are incredibly high—and because you deserve the best. The "old guard" may not have the necessary skills for this next level of your career, and you should have total confidence requiring each member of your Practice Project Team to be unquestionably far above their competitors in motives, skills, integrity, and track record.

But how could you possibly discern which, of all the available vendor choices, could be the best-of-breed?

This is where a group like mine becomes the most valuable player on your team. If you're the CEO of the project, we act as the President. While we never carry an official title of "President," we devote a lot of time to deeply understanding your vision. We then follow your leadership and create direction on your behalf by managing the entire Practice Project Team. With you as CEO, your guidance is handed to us and we create the motivation and coordination with all of the vendors involved. Besides being busy with running your life and maintaining your income with your chair-side career, there are a few reasons for this.

If you had spent your career coordinating contractors, plumbers, attorneys, realtors, marketing agencies, equipment sales specialists, designers, and architects, you could do this too! To put this in perspective, it's like a patient who trusts you with a 12-unit cosmetic case. You have skills and experience that you bring to the patient, but you also coordinate the most excellent outside resources of labs, suppliers, specialists, and other clinical members. You act as President on behalf of the CEO patient.

If the patient were to go directly to the lab on their own, the results could be horrible. If they spoke with your supplier to try to pick out the best materials, and then asked you to piece it all together, the case could be disastrous. That patient probably doesn't have the training and time invested to know all the necessary pieces of the puzzle, but you do. With your years of training, education, experience, and reputation, you will be that patient's trusted President. They will be the CEO who shares their vision and trusts you to create an amazing end result.

That type of process is similar to what our clients experience with their new practice projects. They cast the vision and we implement that vision to create the practice that takes their breath away. They're dentists—wonderful, talented, dedicated clinicians who want an amazing facility to carry them toward their hopes being fulfilled. And a dentist's skill set is in the depth of clinical expertise they've developed. The details you envision in your new practice can surely become a reality, but you must have the right person leading all the vendors to make it come together.

Without a team like ours, you'll be left to "learn on the job." One local dentist recently did his best to choose a nearby contractor who said he understood dental contracting. The result? That doctor, one of the nicest people I know, is now four months behind schedule and almost $45,000 over budget —and that's before the hammers have even started swinging. That's when he called us, asking for some guidance on how to deal with the contractor.

It's a true story that makes my stomach turn, but the choice of Practice Project Team members who haven't been vetted by the right "President" on your team will leave you with losses. The loss of money is painful. The loss of time is irrecoverable.

If something like that happened to you, who would you ask to motivate and redirect the contractor? Not the accountant. Not the banker. Not the marketer.

Our team has been able to save clients hundreds of thousands of dollars, perhaps millions, not to mention lots of time. We do this by starting the project *with* you and on your behalf from the earliest of stages. It starts with you calling us and discussing your vision.

The multiple members of your Practice Project Team are intimately linked to your project, and as a result, they're linked to your future life. They will be the ones creating the space that will provide for your family, your goals, and your dreams.

Some questions you may ask are:

* ❖ Are they good enough for my project?
* ❖ Are you sure?
* ❖ How do you know?

If you determined that you wanted to do this without a team like mine, I would strongly suggest you borrow from my experience. Over the years, I've discovered two broad qualifications that will lead you to the best-of-breed Practice Project Team members. The first considers their knowledge; the second deals with their track record.

Regarding the qualifier of knowledge, the members on your Practice Project Team must be able to coordinate 13 stages of the project on your behalf. Each of these pieces is interconnected with timing and financing. You can find one of my publications on our website named "Grand Opening: The 13 Stages." The publication discusses this topic in greater detail, but in brief, each member of your Practice Project Team must have immense knowledge of the following topics, in chronological order:

1. TARGET

Your target will determine where you are headed with your future practice, and it can be pinpointed by creating clarity of your vision for the future practice you have in mind. Vision for your target should be explored in three categories: Clinical Vision, Financial Vision, and Personal Vision. Within those categories, your Ideal Patient, your income timeline, and your lifestyle plans are all refined and defined in the practice you will soon create.

Each practice owner has a unique vision and personalized set of standards that reflect them. It's here, during Stage 1, that a plan will be created to meet your singular vision.

One of the most fulfilling aspects of helping doctors open new offices is the realization that, with proper planning to reach your vision, we can create a practice that represents you well and makes you proud.

By going through this exercise thoroughly and thoughtfully, you will find improvement as well as enjoyment of each segment of the following 12 stages.

2. FINANCING

Financing can give your practice a dramatic advantage if done properly.

❖ Will you own your real estate or lease?

❖ If you could own dental real estate with no down payment required, would you want to do that?

❖ What is the best strategy to include in your financing of the practice?

❖ At which moments will funding occur for construction, equipment, real estate, and business costs?

❖ Which banks have the best rate and terms?

❖ What budget is needed for your specific project?

❖ What plan will bring your new office to profitability as fast as possible?

❖ When is it imperative you have a good business plan?

With hundreds of valid questions, Stage 2 and financing might have more confusion than any other. My team and I guide you through the complex elements of financing, budgeting, business plans, and forecasting.

The financing discussion is much deeper than knowing the difference between two banks' rates. Plan and budget with accurate numbers, then match your unique vision with lenders who have proven themselves excellent with those kinds of practices.

For our high-level clients, we create business plans and present multi-layered financing proposals to get the kinds of loans normally unavailable to small businesses.

For dentists, one of the biggest surprises is the discovery that many local banks claim to have dental loans, but they find in actuality that only a minority of banks have the specific loans that cater to the needs of a new dental practice. Our field is nuanced and the financing must be custom made for a dental practice project.

3. DEMOGRAPHICS ANALYSIS

The best demographics reports aren't cookie cutter; they're customized to match your vision.

Some of the important demographics and site selection information are found in these pages, but more than a dozen other analytical tools are needed to make wise decisions about the right town for your new office.

Our clients learn about concepts like the Donut Hole Theory, competitive analysis of other doctors, the potential of Insurance Partnering, an alignment of your clinical, financial, and personal vision, and the influential difference between the PDR and the I-PDR.

Don't fall for the factory-created, cheap template demographics reports that are irrelevant in today's dental practices.

With Customized Demographics Reports you will:

- ❖ Access the best precise demographics reports available in dentistry
- ❖ Get complete clarity about the best areas to open your practice
- ❖ Know which areas are projected for rapid growth and profits
- ❖ Find dental-specific information on competition that will protect your practice
- ❖ Get customized reports to match your unique clinical and financial vision

Our team coordinates and translates mountains of data for our clients. Some of that information is covered in these pages, while some is left for deeper analysis.

4. SITE SELECTION

As we have discussed in this book, site selection goes far beyond the look of the building.

For your new office, site selection must take into account:

- ❖ Construction cost controls that vary more than 40% from site to site
- ❖ Landlord concerns
- ❖ Taxation
- ❖ PPOs and reimbursement levels
- ❖ Signage, legal concerns, Vision Alignment, and more

Our high-level clients experience our in-person consulting when we fly into your town and work on your behalf to find the best location for your new practice. Doctors also learn more about site selection with our online training tools and 1-on-1 Guidance Mentoring sessions.

5. FLOOR PLAN AND OFFICE DESIGN

In this stage, you are able to create an environment that fits your clinical vision. But it is important that you aren't fooled by companies who offer this service for "Free."

Too often, we find doctors trapped with vendors who use "free" designs as negotiating leverage *against* doctors. We have found that a "free" set of drawings is often used to convince you that paying much higher prices for things like equipment and construction are better for you.

Doctors should know that when our team creates their floor plans, they're in complete control, able to work with any equipment and construction company. If you like having all your options available, floor plans and office design is a topic to be given careful consideration.

With the best design, you can create the:

❖ Ergonomically proper plan, extending your comfort and career

❖ Highest levels of profit

❖ Smoothest clinical flow pattern

❖ Most enjoyable space for you and your staff

Create a floor plan and design with the 40 points of dental office design to get the most efficient, profitable and clinically excellent office.

6. EQUIPMENT SELECTION

Two factors should be considered with dental equipment:

1. Clinical standards
2. Pricing and negotiation

Will you pay more for the same equipment purchase by a colleague in the same town?

Pricing and negotiation have lead some doctors to pay 20–30% *more* for the *same* equipment. We help clients negotiate the best pricing while knowing what doctors across the country have paid.

The right equipment will support your clinical standards while preserving your chair-side comfort. Since you'll keep this equipment for years, it's important we get you the selections that represent you clinically and protect your ability to practice for years.

The exploration of equipment can be filled with strong opinions from dozens of vendors, which is why getting clear perspective on each option is a top priority.

Your use of an unbiased advisor will be a valuable resource to help you get the best options at the best prices.

7. Construction Bidding

We review, critique, and even negotiate this process, having seen all the tricks and inflated price points. We pinpoint which contractors are of the highest integrity who could be excellent Practice Project Team members.

8. Building Permits

With our design plans, along with the contractor, engineering, and architectural plans, we advise on how other clients have best worked with local building departments.

9. Marketing Plan Commencement

Ensure your new office has new-patient flow that meets your goals.

Marketing is unfortunately put off far too long in many new office projects. The right plans will integrate with your vision and be implemented by the best in the industry.

100 New Patients on Opening Day is a program we are proud of and strive for as we guide doctors through their launch strategy.

When we first meet with clients, we discuss the need to have a marketing plan in place prior to the project's birth. We help coordinate vendors and co-create the marketing plan with clients. This is the stage in which we begin that campaign.

10. CONSTRUCTION

If a contractor is even a few degrees outside of the acceptable range of quality, skills, experience, or integrity, this stage can be the greatest cause of regret. With the right team, this stage can go so well that you tell colleagues and family it was exciting and one of the most fulfilling experiences of your career!

11. EQUIPMENT INSTALLATION

My team coordinates every aspect of this, integrating the installation team and the manufacturing standards to make the high-investment equipment perform at its peak level for you.

12. DRY RUN

Prior to opening day, we advise you to try a full-day dry run where the most gracious of friends and family are the first to experience your new facility. You'll provide great dentistry, and we want to make sure all of your supporting components prop you up the best way possible.

13. GRAND OPENING

Cut the ribbon!

•   •   •

The right "President," working for *you* the CEO, will have a plan in place for every step of your project. They'll anticipate opportunities and problems coming, and they'll be able to coordinate the actions and timing of all the vendors involved. If the lead person on your team is unable to articulate these steps and incorporate your vision into them, look out!

The second qualification that will lead you to the best Practice Project Team members is a bit of a shortcut.

The easiest way to discern this is their willingness and ability to show you—literally "show you"—a minimum of ten projects they're proud of, can take credit for, and that are outstanding. You deserve that. Your family deserves that. Your patients trust you for that. Your legacy deserves it. Accept nothing less and demand the best because this is your defining moment.

There are plenty of competing options for your practice's next five, ten, or fifty years, and you should stand tall with confidence and poise, knowing that you're in one of the most coveted, stable, and reliable businesses. Bankers, property owners, suppliers, and others know the predictable nature of dentistry, and they know you've invested heavily in making your future practice succeed. Choose the team carefully.

As my last thoughts for you, I would like to share a prediction:

You will never see a town through the lens of your dental eyes the same way again.

The thoughts you've developed over these pages have now opened up a new world of possibilities and criteria for you to evaluate practice locations—in a way few have had an opportunity to examine. These tools are proven and effective, so use them, plan with them, and share them with your colleagues so our entire cottage industry can advance with predictable, stable results.

My team is here to help, and we hope to make a difference in the futures of the dentists who grant us their trust, and we also hope to assist in making this your best experience for decades of personal and professional accomplishment.

Our dental community is a wonderful, enjoyable group, and I'm proud to play a small part in its success.

Best of luck to you and your future!

Jayme

• • •

If you're ready to take the next step toward realizing your vision for your future practice and are in need of guidance, please get in touch to discuss how my team can work with you to develop and implement an insightful, profitable plan to suit your needs and wishes:

jayme@HowToOpenADentalOffice.com

For more practice-defining strategies for your new business, visit:

www.HowToOpenADentalOffice.com

And read our blog, packed with hundreds of profit-making, personally empowering tips:

www.HowToOpenADentalOffice.com/blog

RESOURCES

On the following pages, you'll find the four ways we serve and support our clients—doctors just like you who open successful new offices.

Here you'll see everything from free tools accessible right now to customized project management experiences.

With all of our resources, we want to be the most valuable and trusted advisor to assist you in successfully creating the practice you've been dreaming of.

Our goal is to decrease your risks and costs while increasing your success.

OPTION ONE: **Free Resources**

OPTION TWO: **High-Level Training Courses**

OPTION THREE: **1-on-1 Guidance and Mentoring**

OPTION FOUR: **Customized Project Management**

Doctors across the country access these tools to open their new offices.

Which path is best for you?

Explore the next few pages to find out.

— OPTION ONE —

FREE RESOURCES

The Blog

You can find hundreds of examples of free resources on our blog. Thousands of visitors across the world read the articles each month.

www.HowToOpenADentalOffice.com/blog

The Podcast

www.HowToOpenADentalOffice.com/podcast

— OPTION TWO —

HIGH-LEVEL TRAINING COURSES

If you like studying the best methods and implementing them on your own terms, these high-level training programs are a perfect next step.

Understand the deeper levels, methods and strategies used at various stages of opening a new dental office. You'll get practical tools and resources to get you the answers you need.

You can access over a decade worth of experience with a shortcut through these high-level training programs.

www.HowToOpenADentalOffice.com/training

Training for the right decisions in your new practice includes:

- ❖ Black Box Demographics
- ❖ Lease Versus Own: The Real Estate Strategy
- ❖ New Office Timeline: Project Planning
- ❖ Masterful Floor plan Design

Come discover the education you need to open a practice successfully.

www.HowToOpenADentalOffice.com/training

— OPTION THREE —

1-ON-1 GUIDANCE AND MENTORING

Work personally with Jayme as he guides you through each step of the New Office process.

With Jayme as your personal advisor, you'll eliminate confusion and get clear direction, and have access to the resources from the expert team who developed the proven process to open a successful new office.

1-on-1 Guidance and Mentoring programs are a powerful way to give you confidence to open your new office with an expert by your side.

Limited openings are available during enrollment periods.

The formal application process can be found here:

www.HowToOpenADentalOffice.com/Apply

— OPTION FOUR —

CUSTOMIZED PROJECT MANAGEMENT

Experience the most freedom, the least stress, and have an expert team creating your practice who follows your personal vision.

What if you could be involved in the stages you enjoy most while entrusting the completion of your new office to someone you fully trusted?

What if they were capable of giving you clear, successful direction based on your goals?

What if you had an unbiased advisor, motivated only by your happiness, with the office being built on your terms?

If those things sound attractive, then allow our team to manage the project to ensure you have an expert team working for you.

Our team will learn the unique, intimate, and subtle elements that you desire in your new office—and then we'll make it all come together for you.

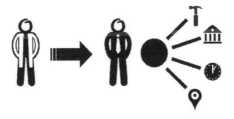

If you're one of the many doctors who knows they can *earn more* and *enjoy more* by working chair-side while we manage your new office project for you, this is the best path.

You will:

- ❖ Outsource major pieces of your project to a team who gets it done right.

- ❖ Leverage your chair-side income by hiring the expert team in new office creation.

- ❖ Avoid wasting time and money on costly pitfalls by using the best methods.

- ❖ Access proven techniques, contacts, and plans instantly.

You'll act as CEO, casting vision for your practice, and our team will act as your president, putting all the pieces in motion on your behalf. This will be your project done on time, on budget and with top quality.

In the coming months, you'll walk through the doors of the practice you've been imagining, stepping proudly into a successful future.

Schedule a strategy session by completing the Customized Project Management Application here:

www.HowToOpenADentalOffice.com/project

ABOUT THE AUTHOR

For nearly a decade, Jayme Amos has worked with dentists, caring for their practice success so they can care best for patients. His blend of experiences in Fortune 500 and entrepreneurial settings has benefited hundreds of dentists with profitable practice growth tools and stunning new practice locations.

Prior to working with his dental clients, Jayme co-founded and grew a million-dollar recruiting firm, earning him a keen understanding of the needs of thriving small businesses. Through his participation in numerous site selections and lease negotiations, he has become a trusted advisor in dentists' new location projects. In addition, he sits as an Advisory Board Member for multiple dental educational facilities and has been invited as a speaker to multiple residency groups, sales organizations, and dental educational facilities.

Jayme resides in the Philadelphia suburbs and keeps his faith, wife, and children as his life's greatest efforts.

www.HowToOpenADentalOffice.com
Jayme@HowToOpenADentalOffice.com

Made in the USA
Columbia, SC
11 May 2019